P9-DDF-145

HALLMARK KEEPSAKE ORNAMENTS

A COLLECTOR'S GUIDE
THIRD EDITION

Hallmark

Clara Johnson Scroggins

ISBN 0-87529-622-X

All prices shown in this book are the original retail prices for the year the ornament was offered.

Contents

Dedication

To all Hallmark collectors, the Houston and Missouri City Chapters of Links, Inc., Henry and Barbara Powell, Meredith DeGood, Jane Jarvis, Alan Forbush, Ron Houk, and all those at Hallmark who have given their time and help so freely.

To Joe, Michael, Michelle, Martha Kathleen, the Johnson Family, and Elizabeth Odom...Thanks.

NOTE TO THE COLLECTOR: This Third Edition of the *Keepsake Ornament Collector's Guide* provides a way for you to keep a record of your ornaments. You will find a small box beside each ornament description. Use the boxes to check off the ornaments in your collection.

Dear Collector Friends,

Welcome to the third edition of the *Keepsake Ornament Collector's Guide*. I hope you find the information about the Keepsake and Keepsake Magic Ornaments helpful and interesting as you pursue your collecting. The most enjoyable aspect of writing this book is sharing what I learn about the ornaments with you.

I believe sharing is what ornament collecting is all about. And I feel very lucky to have so many collector friends across the nation keeping me up to date on the latest trends in collecting and displaying ornaments.

For years I have displayed my own collections on several trees in my home. But now I hear I'm not alone in doing this. We have entered a "multiple-tree" era! Actually, putting up several trees in the home is an Old-World European custom. A long time ago, people decorated a tree for each member of the family and placed the trees in their rooms.

Today many collectors decorate at least two trees — one in the family room and one in the living room. They trim the family room tree with ornaments their children love or ornaments given by family and friends. The living room tree is often more formal. It might be decorated with family heirloom ornaments, limited editions, or designs made of silver or crystal. It is also becoming a widespread practice for people to place a tree in each child's room, trimmed with ornaments that reflect the child's interests. Tabletop trees are gaining popularity and have become a common sight in college dorms and apartments.

Because we live in a mobile world where family and friends reside hundreds of miles apart, an increasing number of collectors are sending Keepsake Ornaments through the mail as gifts. Collectors have found that the ornaments offer a way to communicate with others. Commemorative designs and lifestyle ornaments are given as an expression of caring to people who live nearby or across the miles.

Keepsake Ornament collectors are uniting, meeting and organizing as never before. What an exciting development for this hobby we all love.

Happy Collecting!

Clara Johnson Scroggins

A HISTORY OF COLLECTIBILITY

Hallmark Keepsake Ornaments are among the most widely collected ornaments in the country. The reason why they are more "collectible" than others is hard to pinpoint. But two attributes — integrity and innovation — have played a major role in the ever-expanding collectibility of the Keepsake line.

Integrity is something Hallmark has stood for since the company was founded by Joyce Hall in 1910. This integrity certainly extends to the Keepsake line.

When Hallmark announces that the edition size of an ornament will be 24,700 pieces, collectors are confident that they won't find 24,701 pieces for sale. They also know that Hallmark has strict practices concerning the reissuing of ornaments. Series designs and dated ornaments are never reissued. In fact, approximately ninety-five percent of the Keepsake line is original each year. Those few designs that are reissued come from the preceding year.

The other major factor in the collectibility of the line is innovation. When I use that word, people who are new to collecting Keepsake Ornaments might think I'm referring to the lighted ornaments that feature such electronic wonders as changing scenes and motion. And these collectors would be correct. However, the Keepsake line's history of innovation traces all the way back to its beginnings in 1973.

At one time, Collectible Series and ornaments carrying year dates were rarities. In 1973, Hallmark offered its first series ornament — "Betsey Clark" — and dated it. Collectors loved both ideas. They loved the idea of having a dated design they could connect with a specific time in their life. And they loved the idea of a series ornament they could look forward to finding each year.

The first Betsey Clark series ornament

Ed Seale, sculptor of "Wee Chimney Sweep"

Today, nearly sixty percent of the Keepsake line is dated, and twenty-six Collectible Series have joined that first one. In 1982, Hallmark began marking series ornaments with a tree-shaped symbol and number to help collectors identify each design's place in the series. Again, collectors welcomed this innovation. It led to other markings such as the hand-written number on the 1987 "Christmas is Gentle" ornament and the embossed edition size on the "Holiday Heirloom" design of the same year.

You can see that every innovation in the Keepsake line has led to some later innovation that pleased the collector. For example, the Collectible Series designs cleared the way for limited editions. The success of series ornaments led the Hallmark staff to believe that collectors would enjoy having designs that were issued in limited numbers. How right they were! The 1986 limited edition "Magical Unicorn" was a phenomenal success, and the 1987 Keepsake line included three different limited edition ornaments.

Another group of ornaments that can trace its roots back to Collectible Series is the 1987 "Artists' Favorites" collection. These ornaments are not official series, but they do feature subject matter that has been popular with collectors. They are favorite designs of the Hallmark artists and, like the series ornaments, carry special markings — the artist's signature or initials on each piece.

The wide variety of commemorative ornaments now in the Keepsake line evolved from a 1973 design. That ornament, "Christmas Is Love," carried the first sentiment in the line: "Christmas is love. Christmas is you." This message gave collectors a direct way to express a feeling to a loved one. It was an idea that now seems very traditional and is even taken for granted. But in 1973 it was a new idea and became the forerunner to commemoratives such as "First Christmas Together," "Our Home to Yours," "Mother," and "Friendship."

The styles, the materials, and the formats of Keepsake Ornaments have been continually expanded. Once a collection of glass balls and yarn designs, the Keepsake line is now a spectrum of acrylic, bone china, wood, porcelain and handcrafted formats. There are ornaments for every taste, from collectors who prefer a country look to those who love hi-tech.

The contrast between the first Keepsake line in 1973 and the Keepsake Ornaments collectors love today is dramatic. But what hasn't changed is the sense of surprise and expectation collectors experience each year, knowing the ornaments will offer innovations that will increase their collectibility.

"Holiday Unicorn" — one of the most sought after Keepsake Ornaments

NATIONAL CLUB IS WHAT WE WANTED

It's finally here! The national "Keepsake Ornament Collector's Club" sponsored by Hallmark marks 1987 as its "Charter Year."

Much of the credit for the development of the club must go to you, the collectors. Your calls, letters, and collecting fervor convinced the staff at Hallmark to launch a national club.

I have asked many of my collector friends what benefits they would want from a national club. The enthusiastic responses I received could fill this book from cover to cover! But the two benefits collectors mentioned most often were: inside information about Keepsake Ornaments, and exclusive ornaments available to club members only.

The new club makes both of these wishes come true. Two exclusive Keepsake Ornaments are available to members in the 1987 charter year. The first is a handcrafted "Wreath of Memories" sent to members inside the membership kit. Hallmark has a special name for the club ornament that is included in the kit — "Keepsake of Membership." This ornament is a permanent memento and Hallmark's way of welcoming collectors into the club family.

Duane Unruh, the sculptor of this design, felt it was a privilege to create the charter year "Keepsake of Membership." He brought a wealth of experience to the task, having spent several years sculpting miniature pewter and bronze figurines for Hallmark before he came to Trim-A-Home, the ornament department.

The wreath is a credit to Unruh's expertise in sculpting miniatures. "The design is a milestone for Hallmark," he told me. "In addition to being the first club ornament, it's the first design we've ever decorated with tiny reproductions of Keepsake Ornaments from previous years. They were the perfect trimming for the wreath."

Unruh also mentioned that he was very careful to sculpt recognizable details in the reproductions so members could find their favorites such as the "Rocking Horse" or "Clothespin Soldier." The ornament is dated "1987," displays the club logo in brass, and carries a marking that appears only during the club's first year — "1987 Charter Member."

Keepsake of Membership Ornament — "Wreath of Memories"

Members Only Ornament — "Carousel Reindeer"

The second '87 club ornament is named "Carousel Reindeer." A certificate inside the membership kit entitles charter members to order this "Members Only" design from their Hallmark dealer. Sculpted by Linda Sickman, the ornament features a prancing reindeer inside a hoop. Like the "Wreath of Memories," it carries the club logo, year date, and the identification "1987 Charter Member."

Linda Sickman pointed out that the handcrafted hoop format of this ornament is reminiscent of the 1975 "Nostalgia" Keepsake Ornaments, which she also sculpted. "The 'Carousel Reindeer' captures the appeal of those early Keepsake designs," she said, "but it is more contemporary and elegant. To me, it symbolizes both the rich history of the Keepsake line and the creativity the Hallmark artists put into the ornaments each year."

The other benefit collectors wanted from a national club was information — and lots of it! Through membership, collectors receive exclusive and privileged information direct from the source. There will be no more guessing and no more inaccurate facts.

Named "Collector's Courier," the club newsletter will offer previews of new Keepsake Ornaments, interviews with Hallmark artists, explanations about designs, materials and formats, and articles of special interest to Keepsake collectors.

Since one of the main goals of the club is to unite Keepsake Ornament collectors, the newsletter includes a question-and-answer column and a section for members' letters. I know that collectors who live in remote areas of the country often feel that they don't get the most up-to-date news. Not any more. These collectors will receive the same information as those who live in large cities.

The club brings members even more than exclusive ornaments and news. They receive a personalized membership card, ornament registry, club folder, and other special club materials and mailings.

I can hardly wait to get my charter membership kit. The anticipation is like the feeling we all have just before the Keepsake display goes up in the Hallmark store. The club will bring us this Christmas excitement throughout the year.

1987 Charter Membership Kit

YOU CAN DISPLAY KEEPSAKE ORNAMENTS YEAR-ROUND

One of the nicest traditions of Christmas, collectors say, is sharing ornaments with family and friends. Many collectors have discovered that this tradition can be enjoyed throughout the year. Instead of packing their Keepsake Ornaments away after the holiday season, collectors are displaying them in their homes year-round.

Here are photographs that illustrate just some of the ideas for year-round display that I have received from my collector friends. The possibilities for this kind of display are endless. That's just one more reason to be a Keepsake Ornament collector!

GOING HALLMARKING FOR ORNAMENTS

Collecting Hallmark Keepsake Ornaments has become a favorite American pastime. People are spending weekends and many of their spare hours searching for ornaments to fill gaps in their collections.

Those inflicted with this special fever call themselves "Hallmarkers." And "Going Hallmarking" is the term they use to describe their adventurous trips to out-of-the-way Hallmark shops, department stores, drugstores, antique shops and any nook or cranny that sells or might have sold Hallmark products.

Vacations have become a favorite "Hallmarking" time for entire families. Ornaments are often purchased as souvenirs of a particular trip. And many people find vacation time the perfect opportunity to buy Keepsake Ornaments for friends. Collectors tell me they become very familiar with the empty spots in friends' collections. "It's almost as much fun to surprise a friend with that impossible-to-find design as it is to find one for myself," a collector said.

Hallmark fever now extends well beyond the continental United States to Alaska, Hawaii, Canada and to Americans living abroad. But this collecting fever didn't happen overnight. It has been building ever since Hallmark first offered Keepsake Ornaments in 1973. Year by year, an increasing number of people began to collect Hallmark ornaments. People came to realize that the designs were unique and finely crafted, and they discovered that nearly all of the ornaments were available only one year.

Collectors started to contact Hallmark and each other for background information. Through countless letters and phone calls, people living in one region of the country shared their experiences with those living hundreds of miles away. "Hallmarking" by telephone became a common way to spend an afternoon.

It was only a small step further for collectors to begin meeting in person, and to form local clubs for the purpose of selling, swapping, and trading ornaments, and exchanging stories.

Events for "Hallmarkers" became commonplace. Organized by collectors, the first Hallmark Ornament Collector's Convention was held in July of 1986 in Frankenmuth, Michigan. The collectors and dealers who attended were delighted to share their experiences and knowledge with each other and with the Hallmark staff who were special guests.

The publication of the *Keepsake Ornament Collector's Guides* was another impetus in this collecting fever. Many people received one of the books as a gift and were inspired to start a collection. "I became so interested in the designs," one collector said, "that before I knew it, I was calling the Hallmark store to find out if the ornaments I liked were available. Once I was hooked, there was no turning back."

Indeed, ornament collectors have no desire to turn back because they have discovered that "Hallmarking" is such fun. They have found that ornaments offer a way to mark special occasions, interests and lifestyles. Ornaments even symbolize addictions to other kinds of collectibles! Nearly every train buff I know has a "Tin Locomotive" ornament collection on the tree.

Hallmark's concern for the collector and emphasis on collectibility are particularly gratifying not only to me but to all my collector friends. Hallmark did not originally design Keepsake Ornaments with the collector in mind. The early ornaments were fashioned to be affordable, well-crafted decor items for the home. But collectors fell in love with them. Now the interests and tastes of countless "Hallmarkers" play a major role in the development of Keepsake Ornaments.

THE 1973 COLLECTION

The year 1973 heralded a new dimension in Christmas tree decorating. Until then, Americans had few real choices when decorating their holiday trees. Red, blue, green, silver, and gold glass ball ornaments were the standard. The only way one could "dress up" the family tree was to use tinsel, angel hair, flocking, or garlands of some type.

But in 1973, Hallmark Cards introduced its newest product line — a selection of eighteen specially designed Keepsake Ornaments. Drawing from the talents of its large staff of artists, Hallmark offered six glass ball ornaments with decorative bands and twelve yarn ornaments. More expensive than the basic red, blue, green, silver, and gold balls (and more decorative), Hallmark ornaments were anything but run-of-the-mill. They definitely were destined to become keepsakes. And with this simple beginning, a new holiday tradition of ornament collecting was born.

The 1973 collection included, in the glass ball format, two Betsey Clark designs. One was dated and was first in the series of Betsey Clark ornaments (the longest collectible series made by Hallmark). Another Betsey Clark design was not dated. The four remaining ball ornaments included a manger scene, a Christmas Is Love theme, a drawing of elves, and a design featuring Santa with some of his helpers. The charmingly detailed Yarn ornaments, between four and five inches tall, all retailed for $1.25 (except the Soldier at $1).

Betsey Clark (Musicians), Betsey Clark (First Edition)

Manger Scene, Christmas is Love, Santa with Elves, Elves

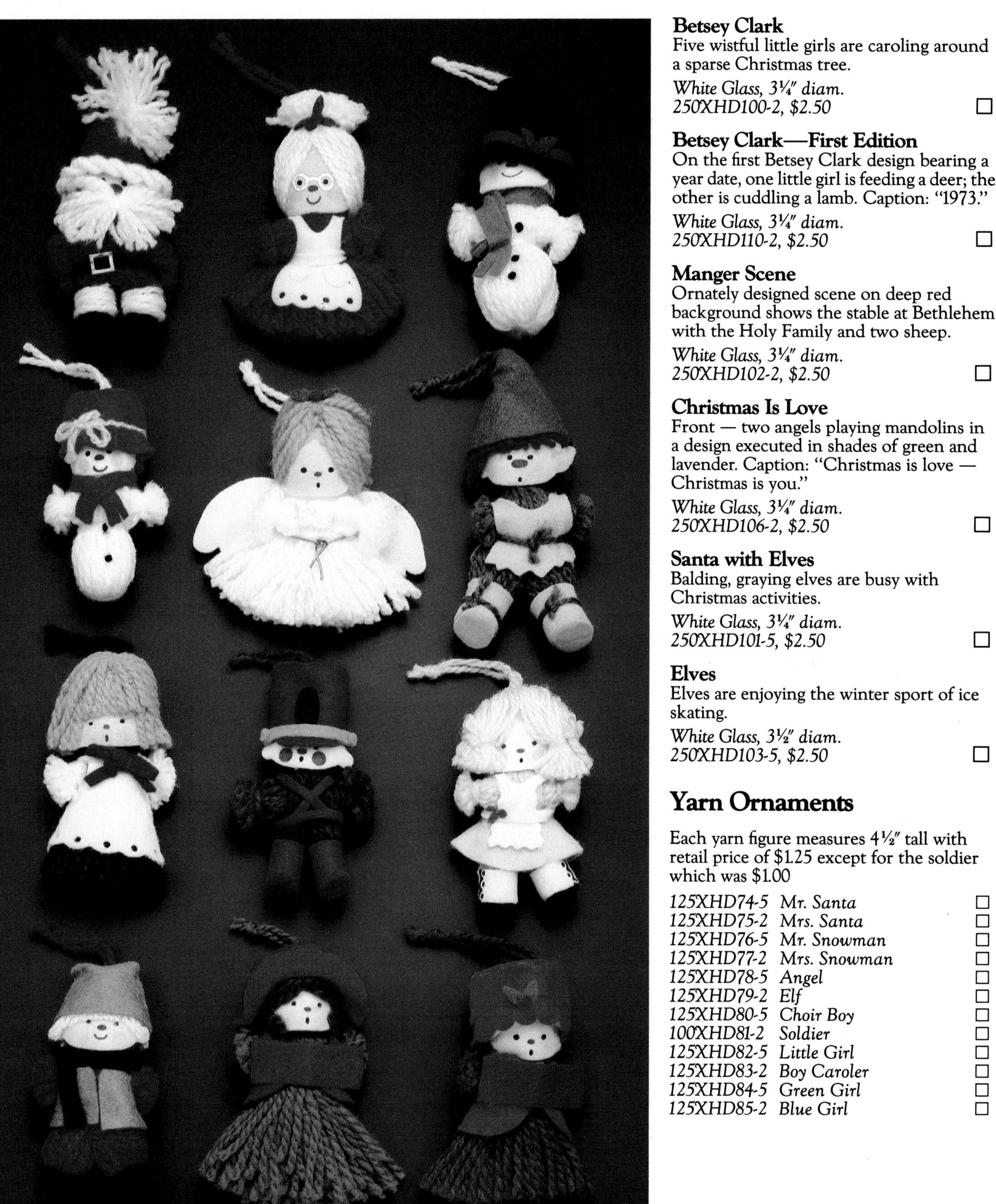

Yarn Ornaments: Mr. Santa, Mrs. Santa, Mr. Snowman, Mrs. Snowman, Angel, Elf, Choir Boy, Soldier, Little Girl, Boy Caroler, Green Girl, Blue Girl

Betsey Clark
Five wistful little girls are caroling around a sparse Christmas tree.

White Glass, 3¼" diam.
250XHD100-2, $2.50 ☐

Betsey Clark—First Edition
On the first Betsey Clark design bearing a year date, one little girl is feeding a deer; the other is cuddling a lamb. Caption: "1973."

White Glass, 3¼" diam.
250XHD110-2, $2.50 ☐

Manger Scene
Ornately designed scene on deep red background shows the stable at Bethlehem with the Holy Family and two sheep.

White Glass, 3¼" diam.
250XHD102-2, $2.50 ☐

Christmas Is Love
Front — two angels playing mandolins in a design executed in shades of green and lavender. Caption: "Christmas is love — Christmas is you."

White Glass, 3¼" diam.
250XHD106-2, $2.50 ☐

Santa with Elves
Balding, graying elves are busy with Christmas activities.

White Glass, 3¼" diam.
250XHD101-5, $2.50 ☐

Elves
Elves are enjoying the winter sport of ice skating.

White Glass, 3½" diam.
250XHD103-5, $2.50 ☐

Yarn Ornaments

Each yarn figure measures 4½" tall with retail price of $1.25 except for the soldier which was $1.00

125XHD74-5 Mr. Santa ☐
125XHD75-2 Mrs. Santa ☐
125XHD76-5 Mr. Snowman ☐
125XHD77-2 Mrs. Snowman ☐
125XHD78-5 Angel ☐
125XHD79-2 Elf ☐
125XHD80-5 Choir Boy ☐
100XHD81-2 Soldier ☐
125XHD82-5 Little Girl ☐
125XHD83-2 Boy Caroler ☐
125XHD84-5 Green Girl ☐
125XHD85-2 Blue Girl ☐

THE 1974 COLLECTION

The tremendous popularity of the 1973 Keepsake Ornaments prompted Hallmark to offer sixteen new designs in 1974.

Dating became more common in 1974 and three ornaments (including the second Betsey Clark 3¼" ornament) carried a holiday date. In addition, Hallmark offered new packaging and introduced two new sizes — 2¼" and 1¾" ball ornaments. The new smaller sizes were offered in sets of two or four, depending upon the ornament design.

Norman Rockwell

On one side Santa is wearing an apron with pockets filled with tools. He is napping in a chair while elves on his lap, shoulder, and all around him are trying to complete the dollhouse that he was building. The other side, "Santa's Good Boys," shows two pajama-clad children engrossed in whatever Santa is telling them.

White Glass, 3¼"
250QX111-1, $2.50 ☐

Norman Rockwell

Father has that "special" tree over his shoulder and his son carries an ax as they triumphantly return from the woods. Caption: "1974."

White Glass, 3¼" diam.
250QX106-1, $2.50 ☐

Betsey Clark - Second Edition

Orchestra and choir of Betsey Clark children are making music. A little girl directs, a boy plays a bass fiddle, a girl plays the banjo, and three are caroling. A garland of holly circles the ornament just above their heads. This is the second dated design in the Betesy Clark series. Caption: "1974."

White Glass, 3¼" diam.
250QX108-1, $2.50 ☐

Charmers

A child decorates a tree; three children are caroling; a girl seems to be reaching for a little bird perched on a branch. Each scene is circled with a garland. Caption: "1974."

White Glass, 3¼" diam.
250QX109-1, $2.50 ☐

Snowgoose

A powerful snowgoose flies above white capped waves with a sailboat in the background. Inspired by Paul Gallico's book, *The Snowgoose.*

White Glass, 3¼" diam.
250QX107-1, $2.50 ☐

Norman Rockwell (Santa), Norman Rockwell (Christmas Tree)

Betsey Clark (Second Edition), Charmers

The Snowgoose, Angel

Raggedy Ann™ and Andy™ *(set of four)*

Little Miracles (set of four)

Buttons and Bo (set of two), Currier and Ives (set of two)

Yarn Ornaments: Santa, Angel, Elf, Snowman, Soldier, Mrs. Santa

Angel

A beautiful Renaissance-type angel is featured on the front and back.

White Glass, 3 1/4" diam.
250QX110-1, $2.50 ☐

Raggedy Ann™ and Raggedy Andy™

Famous pair get ready for Christmas by trimming their tree and exchanging gifts with friends. All ornaments are trimmed at bottom and top with holly garland.

White Glass, 1 3/4" diam.
450QX114-1, 4 per box $4.50 ☐

Little Miracles

Angelic little boy and his rabbit playmate are pictured in four Christmas scenes.

White Glass, 1 3/4" diam.
450QX115-1, 4 per box $4.50 ☐

Buttons & Bo

On one side Buttons & Bo are entwined in ribbon while wrapping a gift. The other side depicts Buttons & Bo leaning against each other with Buttons holding a poinsettia blossom.

White Glass, 2 1/4" diam.
350QX113-1, 2 per box $3.50 ☐

Currier & Ives

Two winter scenes picture a snow-blanketed farmstead and horse-drawn sleigh passing a colonial home.

White Glass, 2 1/4" diam.
350QX112-1, 2 per box $3.50 ☐

Yarn Ornaments

Six colorfully detailed yarn character ornaments, approximately 4 3/4" tall, were offered in 1974 at $1.50 each.

150QX100-1 Mrs Santa ☐
150QX101-1 Elf ☐
150QX102-1 Soldier ☐
150QX103-1 Angel ☐
150QX104-1 Snowman ☐
150QX105-1 Santa ☐

THE 1975 COLLECTION

In 1975, Hallmark expanded its Christmas ornament line to thirty-two models and introduced two new design formats — decorated satin ball ornaments and handcrafted ornaments. Two handcrafted groupings were offered: figurines call "Adorable Adornments" and "Handcrafted Nostaglia Ornaments."

The new satin ball ornaments featured a decorated band. Both of the handcrafted groups were made of sturdy, molded material and were individually hand painted. The colorful figurines had lively expressions, and the Nostalgia collection was distinguished by its antique wood look. Raggedy Ann and Andy™ were added to the Yarn Ornaments collection during this year.

Property Ornaments

Betsey Clark

Four different scenes of Betsey Clark children and the animals and birds associated with Christmas adorn fronts of this set. Backs are dated "Christmas 1975."

White Satin, 2" diam.
450QX168-1, 4 per box $4.50 ☐

Betsey Clark

These paired motifs show a stocking-capped little girl on one ornament and two struggling young skaters on the other. On the backs of both, "Christmas 1975" is surrounded by stars.

White Satin, 2½" diam.
350QX167-1, 2 per box $3.50 ☐

Betsey Clark

Appealing, pajama-clad toddler says bedtime prayers framed by a ring of stars. Caption: "1975."

White Satin, 3" diam.
250QX163-1, $2.50 ☐

Betsey Clark — Third Edition

Front — three little girls dressed in pink, blue, and yellow calico are singing from a songbook they are holding. Back — the book from the front with "Christmas 1975" on the cover. This is the third ornament in the Betsey Clark series.

White Glass, 3¼" diam.
300QX133-1, $3.00 ☐

Currier & Ives

Panoramic snowscene of farmhouse and farm buildings.

White Satin, 3" diam.
250QX164-1, $2.50 ☐

Betsey Clark (set of four), Betsey Clark (set of two)

Betsey Clark Satin Ball, Betsey Clark (Third Edition)

Currier and Ives Satin Ball, Currier and Ives (set of two)

Raggedy Ann™ and Andy™ (set of two), Raggedy Ann™ Satin Ball,

Norman Rockwell Satin Ball,
Norman Rockwell Glass Ball

Charmers, Marty Links™

Currier & Ives

Two Currier & Ives winter scenes are shown on this boxed pair: one of an old mill, the other of a merry group of Victorian ice skaters.

White Glass, 2¼″ diam.
400QX137-1, 2 per box $4.00 ☐

Raggedy Ann™ and Raggedy Andy™

Front — the colorful pair are seated side-by-side in a green wreath which is tied at the top with a red bow. Back — they hold "Merry Christmas" banner. Front of second ornament — they decorate their Christmas tree. Back — garland of holly leaves circles "Christmas 1975."

White Glass, 2¼″ diam.
400QX138-1, 2 per box $4.00 ☐

Raggedy Ann™

Front — Raggedy Ann™ in a ring of poinsettias. Caption on the back: "Christmas 1975" circled by poinsettias.

White Satin, 3″ diam.
250QX165-1, $2.50 ☐

Norman Rockwell

Front — Santa writes in "Good Boys" book while checking on them through a telescope. Back — Santa emerges from a chimney carrying his bag of toys.

White Satin, 3″ diam.
250QX166-1, $2.50 ☐

Norman Rockwell

Front — two small boys are asleep in a wingback chair as Santa peeks from behind. Back — youngster kneels at his bed to say a good-night prayer. Caption: "1975."

White Glass, 3¼″ diam.
300QX134-1, $3.00 ☐

Charmers

Front — tiny barefoot girl in a deep rose-colored dress stands among boughs laden with ornaments. Back — bough and ornaments with "1975" on large center ornament.

White Glass, 3½″ diam.
300QX135-1, $3.00 ☐

Marty Links™

Front — on a beautiful green background, a little girl is kissing an embarrassed little boy's hand as he stands under the mistletoe. Back — in mistletoe wreath center, "Merry Christmas 1975."

White Glass, 3¼″ diam.
300QX136-1, $3.00 ☐

Buttons & Bo

In this coordinated grouping, Buttons & Bo engage in a variety of Christmas activities. The ornaments are dated on the back.

White Glass, 1¾" diam.
500QX139-1, 4 per box $5.00 ☐

Little Miracles

Charming set depicts a wee cherub and his forest friends sharing the joys of Christmas.

White Glass, 1¾" diam.
500QX140-1, 4 per box $5.00 ☐

Yarn Ornaments

Raggedy Ann and Andy™ joined this group of deftly styled yarn characters for the first time in 1975. All are 4½" tall, individually packaged, and priced at $1.75.

175QX121-1	*Raggedy Ann™*	☐
175QX122-1	*Raggedy Andy™*	☐
175QX123-1	*Drummer Boy*	☐
175QX124-1	*Santa*	☐
175QX125-1	*Mrs. Santa*	☐
175QX126-1	*Little Girl*	☐

Handcrafted Ornaments

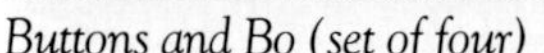

Nostalgia Ornaments

The Nostalgia Ornaments are "rings" crafted of sturdy, molded material and individually hand-painted to resemble antique wood. Motifs evoke memories of Christmas long ago. All are 3¼" in diameter and priced at $3.50.

350QX127-1	*Locomotive (dated)*	☐
350QX128-1	*Rocking Horse*	☐
350QX129-1	*Santa & Sleigh*	☐
350QX130-1	*Drummer Boy*	☐
350QX131-1	*Peace on Earth (dated)*	☐
350QX132-1	*Joy*	☐

Adorable Adornments

Six individually hand-painted characters of intricate design were another first created by Hallmark in 1975. Each are 3½" tall and $2.50

250QX155-1	*Santa*	☐
250QX156-1	*Mrs. Santa*	☐
250QX157-1	*Betsey Clark*	☐
250QX159-1	*Raggedy Ann™*	☐
250QX160-1	*Raggedy Andy™*	☐
250QX161-1	*Drummer Boy*	☐

Buttons and Bo (set of four)

Little Miracles (set of four)

Yarn Ornaments: Drummer Boy, Raggedy Ann™, Raggedy Andy™, Little Girl, Santa Mrs. Santa,

Nostalgia Ornaments: Locomotive, Rocking Horse, Santa and Sleigh

Adorable Adornments: Santa, Mrs. Santa, Drummer Boy

Nostalgia Ornaments: Drummer Boy, Peace on Earth, Joy

Adorable Adornments: Raggedy Ann™, Raggedy Andy™, Betsey Clark

THE 1976 COLLECTION

In 1976, Hallmark added a fourth dimension to its handcrafted ornament offerings — movement. Called "Twirl-Abouts," the unique ornaments had a three-dimensional figure in the center that rotated on a brass pin. Three of the four different Twirl-About designs were dated.

To mark the Bicentennial year, Hallmark also offered a special commemorative ornament in 1976. The glass ball ornament featured Hallmark Charmers characters in 1776 dress and retailed for $2.50.

Also in 1976, Hallmark introduced the Baby's First Christmas ornament, a personalized design that in future years would prove to be the most popular captioned ornament in the Keepsake line.

The first Baby's First Christmas commemorative ornament.

First Commemorative Ornament

Baby's First Christmas

The original Baby's First Christmas ornament, designed to commemorate the birth of babies born in 1976, was a record best seller and introduced a new Christmas tradition to many families. Front — animals and birds are placing gifts for baby under the decorated tree. Caption: "Baby's First Christmas." Back — animals and birds visit smiling baby. Caption: "1976."

White Satin, 3" diam.
250QX211-1, $2.50 ☐

Bicentennial Commemoratives: Bicentennial '76 commemorative, Bicentennial Charmers Colonial Children (set of two)

Betsey Clark (Fourth Edition), Betsey Clark Satin Ball, Betsey Clark (set of three)

Bicentennial Commemoratives

Bicentennial '76 Commemorative

Charmers dressed in the fashions of Christmas 1776, grace the Hallmark Bicentennial special commemorative ornament. Both the ornament and its package are marked "1976 Commemorative."

White Satin, 3" diam.
250QX203-1, $2.50 ☐

Bicentennial Charmers

Front — three Charmers in colonial costume admire a tiny Christmas tree in front of their log cabin homes. Back — a Charmer girl gathers holly leaves. Caption: "Merry Christmas 1976."

White Glass, 3¼" diam.
300QX198-1, $3.00 ☐

Colonial Children

Front — a boy and girl in colonial clothing have made and dressed a snowman. Back — garland, bird, flag, and "Christmas 1976." Front of second design — a group of colonial children brings home a Christmas tree. Back — garland, Christmas tree, squirrel, and "Merry Christmas 1976."

White Glass, 2¼" diam.
400QX208-1, 2 per box $4.00 ☐

Property Ornaments

Betsey Clark — Fourth Edition

Front — two little dressed-up, bonnet-clad girls are framed by floral and ribbon circle. Back — wintry scene of snow-covered homes in a countryside setting. Caption: "Christmas 1976." This is fourth ornament in the Betsey Clark series.

White Glass, 3¼" diam.
300QX195-1, $3.00 ☐

Betsey Clark

Front — little girl warms herself at a potbellied stove. Back — "Christmas 1976."

White Satin, 3" diam.
250QX210-1, $2.50 ☐

Betsey Clark

The three front designs are: Santa and little girl caroling; little girl snow skiing; and a fiddling duet of children. All are dated on the back.

White Satin, 2" diam.
450QX218-1, 3 per box $4.50 ☐

Currier & Ives

Front — a horse-drawn sleigh and skaters on a pond in front of a snow-covered colonial house. A farmyard in winter is shown. Back — Caption: "To Commemorate Christmas 1976."

White Satin, 3" diam.
250QX209-1, $2.50 ☐

Currier & Ives

Two snow scenes entitled "American Winter Scene" and "Winter Pastime." Caption: "To Commemorate Christmas 1976."

White Glass, 3¼" diam.
300QX197-1, $3.00 ☐

Norman Rockwell

Front — Santa is recuperating from his travels; it's "December 25." Back — Santa feeds his reindeers. Caption: "Christmas 1976."

White Glass, 3¼" diam.
300QX196-1, $3.00 ☐

Rudolph and Santa

Front — Rudolph with his "nose so bright" frolics in the snow as Santa watches. Caption: "Rudolph the Red-Nosed Reindeer." Back — a green garland and "Christmas 1976."

White Satin, 2½" diam.
250QX213-1, $2.50 ☐

Raggedy Ann™

Front — Raggedy Ann™ is hanging stockings on the decorated mantle of a glowing fireplace. Back — the stockings are filled, toys from Santa surround the fireplace, and "Merry Christmas 1976" is across the top.

White Satin, 2½" diam.
250QX212-1, $2.50 ☐

Currier and Ives Satin Ball, Currier and Ives Glass Ball

Norman Rockwell, Rudolph and Santa, Raggedy Ann™

Marty Links™ (set of two), Happy the Snowman, Charmers

Chickadees, Cardinals

Marty Links™

Front — smiling girl dressed in red places a gift under the tree. Back — red ball ornament with "Merry Christmas 1976." Front of second design — the "stockings are hung by the chimney with care" and mouse is admonished to be quiet. Back — a bow-topped holly wreath centered with "Noel 1976."

White glass, 2 ½" diam.
400QX207-1, 2 per box $4.00 ☐

Happy the Snowman

Front — on a dark green background the Happy Snowman enjoys the red birds and snowflakes around him. Back — two Happy Snowmen and "Happy Holidays." Front — companion piece shows three snowmen, snowflakes, and holly. Back — three Happy Snowmen one holding a ribbon banner bearing "Merry Christmas."

White Satin, 2 ½" diam.
350QX216-1, 2 per box $3.50 ☐

Charmers

Front of first design: — a boy watches his reflection in a pool. Front of second design: — little Charmer preparing holiday food over glowing campfire. Both are captioned "Christmas 1976."

White Satin, 2 ½" diam.
350QX215-1, 2 per box $3.50 ☐

Decorative Ball Ornaments

Chickadees

Front — two chickadees perch on a bough. Back — one bird perched on a bough. Caption: "Christmas 1976."

White Glass, 2 ⅝" diam.
225QX204-1, $2.25 ☐

Cardinals

Front — two nesting cardinals. Back — one cardinal on spray of evergreen. Caption: "Christmas 1976."

White Glass, 2 ⅝" diam.
225QX205-1, $2.25 ☐

Yesteryears Ornaments: Train, Santa, Partridge, Drummer Boy

Twirl-About Handcrafted Ornaments: Angel, Santa, Partridge, Soldier

Handcrafted Ornaments

Yesteryears

This collection of four, three-dimensional ornaments in "wood look" designs are intricately hand painted to enhance their "old world" character. Newly designed packaging included a gift tag with each ornament. Each ornament was year dated, and was priced at $5.00. Sizes vary from 2¾" to 4" tall.

500QX181-1	*Train*	☐
500QX182-1	*Santa*	☐
500QX183-1	*Partridge*	☐
500QX184-1	*Drummer Boy*	☐

Twirl-Abouts

Twirl-Abouts — three-dimensional ornaments centered with rotating figures on a brass pin — were introduced in 1976. Hand-painted, they are highly sought by collectors. Ranging from 3½" to 4" tall, all were priced at $4.50. Angel, partridge, and soldier bear year dates.

450QX171-1	*Angel*	☐
450QX172-1	*Santa*	☐
450QX173-1	*Soldier*	☐
450QX174-1	*Partridge*	☐

Tree Treats

Tree treats that look good enough to eat were new in 1976. Four ornaments of material resembling baker's dough are another choice for variety and spice in Christmas tree decorations. Tree Treats vary in size from 2¾" to 3⅝" tall and were priced at $3.00. Shepherd and Santa captions: "Season's Greetings 1976." Angel and Reindeer captions: "Merry Christmas 1976."

300QX175-1	*Shepherd*	☐
300QX176-1	*Angel*	☐
300QX177-1	*Santa*	☐
300QX178-1	*Reindeer*	☐

Tree Treats: Shepherd, Angel, Santa, Reindeer

Nostalgia Ornaments: Drummer Boy, Locomotive, Rocking Horse, Peace on Earth

Nostalgia Ornaments

The four reissues of the extremely popular Nostalgia Ornaments introduced the previous year had slight design modifications. Locomotive and Peace on Earth were captioned "Christmas 1976."

400QX128-1	*Rocking Horse*	☐
400QX130-1	*Drummer Boy*	☐
400QX222-1	*Locomotive*	☐
400QX223-1	*Peace on Earth*	☐

Yarn Ornaments

This merry group of six returned in 1976 with very minor changes. All are 4½" tall, individually packaged, and priced at $1.75. (See 1975 Annual Collection.)

175QX121-1	*Raggedy Ann™*
175QX122-1	*Raggedy Andy™*
175QX123-1	*Drummer Boy*
175QX124-1	*Santa*
175QX125-1	*Mrs. Santa*
175QX126-1	*Caroler*

THE 1977 COLLECTION

The year 1977 was one of tremendous expansion for the Hallmark Keepsake Ornament Collection. Three new ornament formats — sewn ornaments with silk-screened designs, acrylic ornaments, and ornaments with the look of stained glass — were introduced. A new decorative cap, with a design exclusive to Hallmark, appeared on glass ball ornaments, and two new colors — gold and chrome — appeared for the first time in the glass ball ornament line.

New commemorative ornaments were offered for Granddaughter, Grandmother, Mother, Love, Grandson, and New Home. And 1977 was the only year Hallmark offered ball ornaments with regional scenes and die cast metal snowflakes.

The Betsey Clark ball ornament (350QX264-2) for this year is especially hard to find. Initially, Hallmark had decided not to offer a Betsey Clark ornament in 1977. Consumer demand was high, however, and the ornament was quickly offered to retailers in August. Due to the delay in production, only a fraction of the normal quantity was distributed.

Commemoratives

Baby's First Christmas

Baby, surrounded by toys, hugs a stuffed bear. Caption: "Baby's First Christmas" and "1977."

White Satin, 3¼" diam.
350QX131-5, $3.50 ☐

Granddaughter

Little girl skates on a pond flanked by trees. Caption: "A Granddaughter is a gift whose worth cannot be measured except by the heart."

White Satin, 3¼" diam.
350QX208-2, $3.50 ☐

Grandson

Front — Santa and toys on a deep blue background. Caption: "A Grandson is...a joy bringer...a memory maker...a Grandson is love."

White Satin, 3½" diam.
350QX209-5, $3.50 ☐

Mother

A motif of pink roses and green holly circle the white glass globe. Caption: "In a Mother's heart, there is love...the very heart of Christmas."

White Glass, 3¼" diam.
350QX261-5, $3.50 ☐

Grandmother

Bordered band encloses a basket of Christmas flowers. Caption: "Grandmother is another word for love."

Gold Glass, 3¼" diam.
350QX260-2, $3.50 ☐

Baby's First Christmas, Granddaughter, Grandson

Mother, Grandmother

First Christmas Together, Love, New Home

First Christmas Together

Front — beautiful Christmas-red background with white circle inset showing two cardinals perched on bare branches. Back — date and caption printed in gold. Caption: "1977" and "Our First Christmas Together."

White Satin, 3¼" diam.
350QX132-2, $3.50 ☐

Love

Front — stained glass window look incorporating "Christmas 1977." Caption: "Love is a golden gift…cherished above all life's treasures."

Gold Glass, 3¼" diam.
350QX262-2, $3.50 ☐

For Your New Home

Front — holiday-decorated red house with 1977 "doormat," patchwork flowers, and checkered border. Back — patchwork flowers and large red heart enclosing caption. Caption: "Christmas fills a home with warmth and love…and memories that last forever.

Gold Glass, 3¼" diam.
350QX263-5, $3.50 ☐

Charmers, Currier and Ives, Norman Rockwell

Property Ornaments

Charmers

Flowers and greenery surround four little children caroling. Caption: "We wish you a Merry Christmas. 1977."

Gold Glass, 3¼" diam.
350QX153-5, $3.50 ☐

Currier & Ives

Shows the Currier & Ives paintings "The Old Grist Mill" and "Trotting Cracks on the Snow." Caption: "1977."

White Satin, 3¼" diam.
350QX130-2, $3.50 ☐

Norman Rockwell

Four favorite Rockwell designs of Christmas activities are reproduced in separate panels. Caption: "Christmas 1977."

White Glass, 3¼" diam.
350QX151-5, $3.50 ☐

Disney Satin Ball, Disney (set of two)

DISNEY
Mickey's head, framed by a wreath, is flanked by Donald Duck and Goofy. Caption: "Merry Christmas 1977."

White Satin, 3¼″ diam.
350QX133-5, $3.50 □

DISNEY
Design 1: Mickey Mouse in a Santa suit gives Minnie Mouse her Christmas gift. Caption: "Merry Christmas." Design 2: Donald Duck pulls Huey, Luey, and Duey on a present-laden sled. Caption: "Happy Holidays."

White Satin, 2¼″ diam.
400QX137-5, 2 per box $4.00 □

Betsey Clark—Fifth Edition
By popular demand the 1977 Betsey Clark ornament was added to the line at the last minute. This design is particularly scarce due to a limited production run. Front — three carolers around a songbook. Back — little girl feeding the birds. Caption: "The truest joys of Christmas come from deep inside" and "Christmas 1977."

White Glass, 3¼″ diam.
350QX264-2, $3.50 □

Betsey Clark (Fifth Edition)

PEANUTS® Glass Ball, PEANUTS® Satin Ball, PEANUTS® (set of two)

PEANUTS® Collection

In 1977, the PEANUTS® gang from Charles Schulz's world-famous cartoon strip was introduced by Hallmark as exclusive additions to the Keepsake Ornament line. Glass and satin ornaments were cleverly packaged in SNOOPY'S Christmas-decorated doghouse.

PEANUTS®

Front — Charlie Brown and his sister Sally watch the empty stockings hanging from the fireplace. A decorated tree is in the background. Back — Schroeder plays the piano as Lucy presents him with a gift. Caption: "A watched stocking never fills" and "Merry Christmas."

White Glass, 2⅝" diam.
250QX162-2, $2.50 ☐

PEANUTS®

Charlie Brown and Lucy have built a snowman who holds a snow shovel. SNOOPY is tangled in Christmas tree lights while Woodstock dressed as Santa stands on a gift. Both are watching the Christmas tree. Caption: "1977."

White Satin, 3¼" diam.
350QX135-5, $3.50 ☐

PEANUTS®

Design 1: SNOOPY as Santa is being pulled in the sleigh by Woodstock and his flock. Design 2: Charlie Brown, Linus, Woodstock, SNOOPY, and Peppermint Patty are building a snowman, having a snowball fight, and ice skating.

White Glass, 2¼" diam.
400QX163-5, 2 per box $4.00 ☐

Grandma Moses

Two beautiful New England village snowscenes from the Grandma Moses paintings "Sugartime" and "Green Sleigh" are shown. A pamphlet giving the history of Grandma Moses and her beloved paintings was included with each gift packaged ornament.

White Glass, 3¼" diam.
350QX150-2, $3.50 ☐

Grandma Moses (Shown with enclosure card)

Christmas Expressions Collection: Bell, Ornaments, Mandolin, Wreath

The Beauty of America Collection: Mountains, Desert, Seashore, Wharf

Rabbit, Squirrel

Christmas Mouse, Stained Glass

Christmas Expressions Collection

Bell

Beautifully decorated bell blanketed with flowers and festooned with ribbons. Caption: "I heard the bells on Christmas Day/ Their old familiar carols play/ And wild and sweet, the words repeat/ Of peace on earth, good will to men. Henry Wadsworth Longfellow."

White Glass, 3 1/4" diam.
350QX154-2, $3.50 ☐

Ornaments

Banded ornament has beautiful array of Christmas ornaments with evergreens, ribbons and bows. Caption: "The spirit of Christmas is peace...the message of Christmas is love. Marjorie Frances Ames."

White Glass, 3 1/4" diam.
350QX155-5, $3.50 ☐

Mandolin

A mandolin and horns are nestled among Christmas greenery. Caption: "Sing a song of seasons; Something bright in all...Robert Louis Stevenson."

White Glass, 3 1/4" diam.
350QX157-5, $3.50 ☐

Wreath

A magnificent green wreath is bedecked with colorful ribbons and bows. Caption: "Christmas is a special time./ A season set apart — / A warm and glad remembering time,/ A season of the heart. Thomas Malloy."

White Glass, 3 1/4" diam.
350QX156-2, $3.50 ☐

The Beauty of America Collection

Mountains

Majestic snowcapped mountains with snow on the roofs of homes seen in the valley. Caption: "The spirit of Christmas is peace...the message of Christmas is love."

White Glass, 2 5/8" diam.
250QX158-2, $2.50 ☐

Desert

A desert mission and a golden sunset. Caption: "Ring out Christmas Bells...and let all the world hear your joyful song."

White Glass, 2 5/8" diam.
250QX159-5, $2.50 ☐

Seashore

Palm trees on a sandy shore, blue skies, and a sailboat regatta. Caption: "Christmas is — the company of good friends, the warmth of goodwill, and the memory of good times."

White Glass, 2 5/8" diam.
250QX160-2, $2.50 ☐

Wharf

Front — tranquil winter scene of homes near the wharf. Back — oceanside view of lighthouse. Caption: "Christmas...when the world stands silent and the spirit of hope touches every heart."

White Glass, 2 5/8" diam.
250QX161-5, $2.50 ☐

Decorative Ball Ornaments

Rabbit

A rabbit is engrossed with a little bird on a broken tree limb. Caption: "Nature's ever-changing beauty brings never-ending joy. Karl Lawrence."

White Satin, 2 5/8" diam.
250QX139-5, $2.50 ☐

Squirrel

A little squirrel seems to be lucky — he has found food in the snow. A cardinal watches. Caption: "Each moment of the year has its own beauty...Emerson."

White Satin, 2 5/8" diam.
250QX138-2, $2.50 ☐

Christmas Mouse

On soft blue background, Mr. and Mrs. Mouse put the finishing touches to their Christmas tree. Caption: "Tinsel and lights make the season so bright."

White Satin, 3 1/4" diam.
350QX134-2, $3.50 ☐

Stained Glass

The sleeve design is in the look of Art Deco stained glass. Caption: "Merry Christmas 1977."

Chrome Glass, 3 1/4" diam.
350QX152-2, $3.50 ☐

Colors of Christmas

Stained Glass Look

Four designs with the jeweled colors of leaded stained glass were introduced to the line in 1977. Made of acrylic, each measures 3¼″ in diameter, with price of $3.50, each. All except the bell bear year date, 1977.

350QX200-2	*Bell*	☐
350QX201-5	*Joy*	☐
350QX202-2	*Wreath*	☐
350QX203-5	*Candle*	☐

Holiday Highlights Collection

A collection of four unbreakable clear acrylic ornaments with the look of hand engraved crystal featured scenes and messages reflecting traditional Christmas sentiments.

Joy

Large letters spelling "JOY," with the center "O" filled with fruit. Background is delicate scrolling. Caption: "JOY 1977."

Acrylic, 3¼″ diam.
350QX310-2, $3.50 ☐

Peace on Earth

A snug village scene with snow-covered houses, pine trees, and a church in the center with its spire reaching for the moonlit sky. Caption: "Peace on earth, good will toward men. 1977."

Acrylic, 3¼″ diam.
350QX311-5, $3.50 ☐

Drummer Boy

A drummer boy marches as he beats the drum. Caption: "Rum-pa-pum-pum" repeated four times around the border.

Acrylic, 3¼″ diam.
350QX312-2, $3.50 ☐

Star

The star at the top casts etched beams of light that radiate over the ornament's surface. Caption: "Once for a shining hour heaven touched earth."

Acrylic, 3¼″ diam.
350QX313-5, $3.50 ☐

Colors of Christmas: Bell, Candle, Joy, Wreath

Holiday Highlights: Joy, Peace, Drummer Boy, Star

Snowflake Collection

Twirl-About Ornaments: Snowman, Weather House, Bellringer, Della Robia Wreath

Metal Ornaments

Snowflake Collection

A set of four 2⅛″ snowflake die-cast in lightweight, chrome plated zinc were cleverly packaged in peek-through gift box which was accompanied by its own mailing box. This is the only year the snowflake set was offered.

Chrome Plated Zinc, 2⅛″ diam.
500QX210-2, 4 per box $5.00 ☐

Twirl-About Collection

Snowman

Three-dimensional snowflake has snowman that rotates in circular center. The snowman wears a handpainted rakish hat, a red scarf around his neck, and a happy smile. Caption: "1977."

Handcrafted, 3¾″ tall
450QX190-2, $4.50 ☐

Weather House

A timbered house with red-orange roof, double doorways, and shuttered window has hand-painted hearts and flowers trim. Swiss-clad boy and girl rotate in and out of the doorways. Caption: "1977."

Handcrafted, 3 15/16″ tall
600QX191-5, $6.00 ☐

Bellringer

Little boy strikes a bell as he rotates inside an arched gate that is scrolled at the top and decorated on each side with large red bows. Sleigh full of toys and his dog are outside the gate.

Handcrafted, 3 11/16″ tall
600QX192-2, $6.00 ☐

Della Robia Wreath

Little girl, kneeling in prayer, twirls in center of traditional Della Robia wreath. Caption: "1977."

Handcrafted, 3 9/16″ tall
450QX193-5, $4.50 ☐

Nostalgia Collection

The Nostalgia Collection is intricately molded and hand painted to create ring-shaped designs with a wooden, antique look. Individual packages included a gift tag.

Angel

Wide outer ring carries caption, flowers, and symbols with natural hand-carved look. In the center is a flying angel dressed in blue and blowing a horn. Caption: "Peace on earth" and "Good will toward men".

Handcrafted, 3 1/4" diam.
500QX182-2, $5.00 ☐

Toys

A stuffed bear with colorful, steaming locomotive and toy soldier occupy center of red and yellow ring. Caption: "1977."

Handcrafted, 3 1/4" diam.
500QX183-5, $5.00 ☐

Antique Car

Green antique car trimmed in red and yellow with its rumble seat filled with gift forms the center design. Caption: "Season's Greetings 1977."

Handcrafted, 3 1/4" diam.
500QX180-2, $5.00 ☐

Nativity

In the center of the ring is a star-topped stable sheltering the Holy Family and animals. A pine tree is on each side. Caption: "O come let us adore Him."

Handcrafted, 3 1/4" diam.
500QX181-5, $5.00 ☐

Nostalgia Collection: Angel, Toys, Antique Car, Nativity

Yesteryears Collection: Angel, Reindeer, Jack-in-the-Box, House

Cloth Doll Ornaments: Angel, Santa

Yesteryears Collection

Angel

Smiling angel with arms outstretched is hand painted in gay, folk art style. Caption: "Joy to the world 1977."

Handcrafted, 3½″ tall
600QX172-2, $6.00 ☐

Reindeer

Reindeer on wheels, with the nostalgic look of hand painted child's toy. Caption: "1977."

Handcrafted, 4¼″ tall
600QX173-5, $6.00 ☐

Jack-in-the-Box

Jack, hand painted in green, blue and red has sprung up in the open red and pink box. Captures the look of antique, hand-carved wooden toy. Caption: "Merry Christmas 1977."

Handcrafted, 3 13/16″ tall
600QX171-5, $6.00 ☐

House

Hand painted cottage features red roof and shuttered windows with painted designs on the red shutters. Fanlighted door is flanked by Christmas trees. Caption: "Happy Holidays 1977."

Handcrafted, 3 11/16″ tall
600QX170-2, $6.00 ☐

Cloth Doll Ornaments

These are the first two designs made from silk-screened cloth which is stuffed and then quilted.

Angel

A sweet angel with wings spread. Her wings are quilted and there is lace edging on the bottom of her dress.

Cloth, 4″ tall
175QX220-2, $1.75 ☐

Santa

Plump jolly Santa is "Laying a finger beside his nose." A jingle bell is attached to his hat.

Cloth, 4″ tall
175QX221-5, $1.75 ☐

THE 1978 COLLECTION

The Hallmark Keepsake Collection continued to gain in popularity as collectibles when the 1978 line was introduced. This year, a design by Joan Walsh Anglund© joined the other exclusive properties held by Hallmark.

The popular Carrousel collectible series began in 1978 with a dated carrousel of children's toys. Chrome plated chimes were introduced in 1978 and Spencer Sparrow made his debut on ornaments. This also was the initial year of the 25th Christmas Together ornament, and the first year that ecru appeared as a color on soft-sheen satin ball ornaments. The smaller-sized ball ornaments made their last appearance in 1978.

Baby's First Christmas, Granddaughter, Grandson

First Christmas Together, Twenty-fifth Christmas Together, Love.

Grandmother, Mother, New Home

PEANUTS® Collection: Snoopy and Woodstock, Joy to the World, Snoopy as Santa, A Delightful Christmas

Commemoratives

Baby's First Christmas

Baby dressed in yellow is on a blanket playing with a kitten and a stuffed teddy bear. Caption: "Baby's First Christmas 1978."

White Satin, $3\frac{1}{4}$″ diam.
350QX200-3, $3.50 ☐

Granddaughter

On a deep red background an adorable girl decorates her Christmas tree. Caption: "A Granddaughter...never far from thought, ever near in love."

White Satin, $3\frac{1}{4}$″ diam.
350QX216-3, $3.50 ☐

Grandson

Raccoons are sledding, ice skating, and building a snowman. Caption: "A Grandson is loved in a special way for the special joy he brings."

White Satin, $3\frac{1}{4}$″ diam.
350QX215-6, $3.50 ☐

First Christmas Together

Folk art design of red hearts, fruits, flowers, greenery, and a pair of red birds. Caption: "Sharing is the heart of loving" and "First Christmas Together 1978."

White Satin, $3\frac{1}{4}$″ diam.
350QX218-3, $3.50 ☐

25th Christmas Together

Front — flower-entwined "25th Christmas Together," white doves, wedding bells, "1953" and "1978" year dates. Caption on back: "Time endears but cannot fade The memories that love has made."

White Glass, $3\frac{1}{4}$″ diam.
350QX269-6, $3.50 ☐

Love

Birds hover over central heart motif enclosing year date, with poinsettias and berry laden boughs completing design. Caption: "Of life's many treasures, the most beautiful is love" and "1978."

Gold Glass, $3\frac{1}{4}$″ diam.
350QX268-3, $3.50 ☐

Grandmother

Deep red American Beauty roses and holly leaves. Caption: "A Grandmother has a special way of bringing joy to every day."

White Satin, $3\frac{1}{4}$″ diam.
350QX267-6, $3.50 ☐

Mother

Blue flowers and caption, white frosty snowflakes on a silvery white background. Caption: "The wonderful meaning of Christmas is found in a Mother's love" and "Christmas 1978."

White Glass, $3\frac{1}{4}$″ diam.
350QX266-3, $3.50 ☐

For Your New Home

A brightly lighted window shows a beautiful wreath with a glowing candle. Caption: "Home...where the light of love shines brightest." and "Christmas 1978."

White Satin, $3\frac{1}{4}$″ diam.
350QX217-6, $3.50 ☐

PEANUTS® Collection

PEANUTS®

SNOOPY and Woodstock bring their freshly cut tree home and decorate it. Caption: "1978."

White Satin, $2\frac{5}{8}$″ diam.
250QX204-3, $2.50 ☐

PEANUTS®

Linus holds a dated wreath while the rest of the PEANUTS® gang sing "Joy to the World." Caption: "Joy to the World 1978."

White Satin, $3\frac{1}{4}$″ diam.
350QX205-6, $3.50 ☐

PEANUTS®

Front — SNOOPY, Woodstock, and his flock are playing in a toy store. Back — SNOOPY plays Santa as he hangs a filled stocking on the mantle. Caption: "1978."

White Satin, $3\frac{1}{4}$″ diam.
350QX206-3, $3.50 ☐

PEANUTS®

Charlie Brown is all wrapped up in the Christmas tree lights by Woodstock as SNOOPY decorates his doghouse. Caption: "Have a delightful Christmas."

White Satin, $2\frac{5}{8}$″ diam.
250QX203-6, $2.50 ☐

Property Ornaments

Betsey Clark — Sixth Edition

A little girl is at home wrapping a gift...then she is all dressed up and has delivered the present to a friend. This is the first ornament to use the new ecru soft-sheen satin. Caption: "The Christmas spirit seems to bring a cheerful glow to everything" and "1978."

Ecru Soft-Sheen Satin, 3¼" diam.
350QX201-6, $3.50 ☐

Joan Walsh Anglund©

Front — Anglund children are caroling in the snow. Back — they are decorating a snow-covered tree. Caption: "As long as we have love and friends, Christmas never really ends 1978."

White Satin, 3¼" daim.
350QX221-6, $3.50 ☐

Spencer Sparrow

Front — Spencer sits in a wreath. Back — Spencer is pulling a sled loaded with gifts. Caption: "Holly days are jolly days" and "Christmas 1978."

Ecru Soft-Sheen Satin, 3¼" diam.
350QX219-6, $3.50 ☐

DISNEY

Disney characters ride on a wooden train with bell ringing Mickey Mouse dressed as Santa. Dated 1978.

White Satin, 3¼" daim.
350QX207-6, $3.50 ☐

Decorative Ball Ornaments

Merry Christmas (Santa)

Front — Santa and his reindeer soar over rooftops on Christmas Eve. Back — a jolly Santa shoulders his pack. Caption: "Merry Christmas" and "1978."

White Satin, 3¼" diam.
350QX202-3, $3.50 ☐

Hallmark's Antique Card Collection Design

Bells, holly, and ornate lettering are reproduced from an antique card in Hallmark's Collection. Caption: "Christmas is a special time, a season set apart — a warm and glad remembering time, a season of the heart."

Ecru Soft-Sheen Satin, 3¼" diam.
350QX220-3, $3.50 ☐

Betsey Clark-Sixth Edition, Joan Walsh Anglund, Spencer Sparrow, DISNEY

Merry Christmas, Antique Card, Yesterday's Toys, Nativity

The Quail, Drummer Boy, Joy

Holiday Highlights: Snowflake, Santa, Dove, Nativity

Yesterday's Toys

Toys of yesterday circle the band of the ornament. Caption: "Every joy of yesterday is a memory for tomorrow. 1978."

Gold Glass, 3¼" diam.
350QX250-3, $3.50 ☐

Nativity

A beautiful Old World Nativity scene is displayed on a rich blue background. Caption: "The joy of heaven is come to earth."

White Glass, 3¼" diam.
350QX253-6, $3.50 ☐

The Quail

A magnificent quail is depicted in his own habitat. Caption: "Nature has a wonderful way of making a wonder-filled world. 1978."

Gold Glass, 3¼" diam.
350QX251-6, $3.50 ☐

Drummer Boy

A little drummer boy, followed by sheep and geese, marches to the beat of his own drum to where the Christ Child lies in a manger. Caption: "1978."

Gold Glass, 3¼" diam.
350QX252-3, $3.50 ☐

Joy

Front — the word, "Joy," sprigged with holly, is incorporated in a leaded stained-glass-effect oval. Back — Christmas message is enclosed in matching oval. Caption: "Joy" and "The beauty of Christmas shines all around us."

White Glass, 3¼" diam.
350QX254-3, $3.50 ☐

Holiday Highlights

In 1978, the elegant Holiday Highlights group featured four designs with the look of hand-cut crystal. Of unbreakable acrylic, they ranged from 2 11/16" to 3⅝" tall and were priced at $3.50, each. The snowflake motif was dated.

350QX307-6 Santa ☐
350QX308-3 Snowflake ☐
350QX309-6 Nativity ☐
350QX310-3 Dove ☐

Reindeer Chimes

Holiday Chimes

Reindeer Chimes

Three prancing reindeer suspended from a large snowflake are a glistening Christmas mobile. A new format for 1978.

Chrome-plated brass, 5½" tall
450QX320-3, $4.50 ☐

Little Trimmers

Thimble Series (Mouse) — First Edition

Little white mouse wearing a red cap is peeking out of a silver colored thimble. This ornament was the first edition in the Thimble Series.

Handcrafted, 1¾" tall
250QX133-6, $2.50 ☐

Santa

Waving Santa holds a gift wrapped in blue and tied in red ribbon.

Handcrafted, 2¼" tall
250QX135-6, $2.50 ☐

Praying Angel

Angel in pink gown is kneeling in prayer.

Handcrafted, 2" tall
250QX134-3, $2.50 ☐

Drummer Boy

Drummer boy dressed in red, green, and blue is beating his drum.

Handcrafted, 2 1/16" tall
250QX136-3, $2.50 ☐

Little Trimmer Collection

Miniature versions of Thimble Mouse, Praying Angel, Drummer Boy, and Santa were offered as a boxed set. (Not shown)

Handcrafted, 4 per box
900QX132-3, $9.00 ☐

Colors of Christmas

Merry Christmas

A luscious oval Christmas ornament in red, green, yellow, and white. Caption: "Merry Christmas 1978."

Acrylic, 4⅛" tall
350QX355-6, $3.50 ☐

Locomotive

Red train framed in blue, green, and yellow. Caption: "1978."

Acrylic, 3¼" diam.
350QX356-3, $3.50 ☐

Angel

An angel wearing red dress and halo with golden hair and wings.

Acrylic, 3⅝" tall
350QX354-3, $3.50 ☐

Candle

Lovely red candle with glowing flame is banked with holly and berries.

Acrylic, 3⅝" tall
350QX357-6, $3.50 ☐

Handcrafted Ornaments

Dove

Majestic white dove twirls in the center of the white lacy snowflake. Caption: "1978."

Handcrafted, 3 9/16" tall
450QX190-3, $4.50 ☐

Holly and Poinsettia Ball

Large ball with the look of intricate hand carving is circled with large poinsettias and holiday greenery.

Handcrafted, 3½" diam.
600QX147-6, $6.00 ☐

Schneeberg Bell

An elegant reproduction of an intricate Schneeberg wood carving collage. This design used eighty-two decorating processes to achieve the natural wood look. Caption: "Merry Christmas 1978."

Handcrafted, 4" tall
800QX152-3, $8.00 ☐

Angels

Angels twirl about decorating a Christmas tree. Caption: "1978."

Handcrafted, 3⅞" tall
800QX150-3, $8.00 ☐

Thimble Series - First Edition, Santa, Praying Angel, Drummer Boy

Colors of Christmas: Merry Christmas, Train, Angel, Candle

Dove, Holly and Poinsettia Ball, Schneeberg Bell, Angels

Carrousel Series - First Edition

Joy, Angel, Calico Mouse, Red Cardinal

Carrousel Series — First Edition
Hand painted in red, yellow, blue, and green, carrousel has toys that spin around. Made in the look of hand-carved wood, this is the first model in the Carrousel series. Caption: "Christmas 1978" is painted around the top.

Handcrafted, 3" tall
600QX146-3, $6.00 ☐

Joy
Little elfin boy dressed in blue is popping through the center letter "O" of the word "Joy." Hand-painted "bread dough" letters are red trimmed with white.

Handcrafted, 4 3/16" tall
450QX138-3, $4.50 ☐

Angel
Handcrafted, bread-dough look barefoot angel is dressed in blue and holds a star.

Handcrafted, 2 15/16" tall
450QX139-6, $4.50 ☐

Panorama Ball, Skating Raccoon, Rocking Horse, Animal Home

Calico Mouse

Smiling red calico mouse with green ears and nose holds sprig of green holly.

Handcrafted, 3 7/16" tall
450QX137-6, $4.50 ☐

Red Cardinal

This clip-on Cardinal perches realistically on the branches of the Christmas tree.

Handcrafted, 4" tall
450QX144-3, $4.50 ☐

Panorama Ball

Little boy dressed in red has fallen on the ice after he skated a holiday greeting. In the snow-covered background are a fence and trees. Scene is viewed through the peek-through window of this white ornament. Caption: "Merry Christmas 1978," is skate-written on the pond.

Handcrafted, 3 5/8" diam.
600QX145-6, $6.00 ☐

Skating Raccoon

Ice-skating raccoon wears red mittens and scarf and real metal skates.

Handcrafted, 2 3/4" tall
600QX142-3, $6.00 ☐

Rocking Horse

Hand painted polka-dot horse with flying white yarn mane and red rockers has the look of hand-carved wood. Caption: "1978."

Handcrafted, 3 9/16" tall
600QX148-3, $6.00 ☐

Animal Home

A family of mice has taken residence in a precious little mushroom with red shuttered windows, garlanded doorway, and stone steps. Mr. Mouse is in the doorway and Mrs. Mouse is inside.

Handcrafted, 2 9/16" tall
600QX149-6, $6.00 ☐

Yarn Collection

The collection of four Yarn ornaments for 1978 were all 4 1/2" tall, individually packaged, and priced at $2.00

200QX123-1	Green Boy	☐
200QX125-1	Mrs. Claus	☐
200QX126-1	Green Girl	☐
200QX340-3	Mr. Claus	☐

Yarn Collection: Mrs. Santa, Santa, Green Boy, Green Girl

THE 1979 COLLECTION

Two new commemorative ball ornaments for Teacher and Special Friend joined the greatly enlarged Hallmark Keepsake Ornament Collection in 1979.

By then, Baby's First Christmas satin ball ornaments had become solid sellers. In response to consumer demand, Hallmark expanded the Baby's First Christmas offering to include a handcrafted design which was in the form of a green-and-white knitted stocking filled to overflowing with baby toys.

Three new collectible series were inaugurated this year — the dated ceramic bell ornaments, Santa-in-a-vehicle ornaments, and SNOOPY panorama ball ornaments.

Ball ornaments were given new packages in 1979, and nearly 60 percent of the ornaments were dated.

Commemoratives

Baby's First Christmas

Front — toys and gifts for Baby ride a sleigh pulled by animal friends. Back — Baby's toys surround Christmas tree being trimmed by birds. Caption: "Baby's First Christmas 1979."

White Satin, 3 1/4" diam.
350QX208-7, $3.50 ☐

Baby's First Christmas

A real green-and-white knitted stocking is filled with toys for baby. The first time Baby's First Christmas commemorative was offered in the handcrafted ornaments. Caption: "Baby's First Christmas 1979."

Handcrafted, 4" tall
800QX154-7, $8.00 ☐

Grandson

Stocking-capped SNOOPY and Woodstock are sledding in the snow. Caption: "A Grandson...a special someone whose merry ways bring extra joy to the holidays. Christmas 1979."

White Satin, 3 1/4" diam.
350QX210-7, $3.50 ☐

Granddaughter

A little girl, warmly dressed for the weather, is feeding red birds, rabbits, and squirrels in the snow. Caption: "A Granddaughter fills each day with joy by filling hearts with love. 1979."

White Satin, 3 1/4" diam.
350QX211-9, $3.50 ☐

Mother

An abundance of white poinsettias and small blossoms band the ornament and form the message. Caption: "It's love that makes Christmas so special — and Mother who makes us feel loved."

White Glass, 3 1/4" diam.
350QX251-9, $3.50 ☐

Baby's First Christmas: Satin Ball, Handcrafted

Grandson, Granddaughter, Mother, Grandmother

First Christmas Together, Twenty-Fifth Anniversary, Love

Friendship, Teacher, New Home

Grandmother

Little birds enjoy the nectar from a basket of flowers. Caption: "Grandmothers bring happy times — time and time again" and "1979."

White Glass, 3 1/4" diam.
350QX252-7, $3.50 ☐

Our First Christmas Together

Golden wedding bells with ribbon bows and poinsettias with greenery are shown against a dark green background. Caption: "Our First Christmas Together 1979" and "Christmas and Love are for sharing."

Gold Glass, 3 1/4" diam.
350QX209-9, $3.50 ☐

Our Twenty-Fifth Anniversary

White satin ribbon entwines wedding bells, wedding rings, and garland of Christmas greenery. Caption: "Year of our Twenty-Fifth Anniversary 1979. Those warm times shared in past Decembers...The mind still sees, the heart remembers."

White Glass, 3 1/4" diam.
350QX250-7, $3.50 ☐

Love

Light scrolling, white snowflakes, red Gothic printing, and green holly and white background. Caption: "Love...warm as candleglow, wondrous as snowfall, welcome as Christmas" and "Christmas 1979."

White Glass, 3 1/4" diam.
350QX258-7, $3.50 ☐

Friendship

Front — friends are skating on a large frozen pond beside an old mill. Back — a sleighride along a country road. Caption: "There is no time quite like Christmas for remembering friendships we cherish" and "Christmas 1979."

White Glass, 3 1/4" diam.
350QX203-9, $3.50 ☐

Teacher

Front — a raccoon writes message to teacher on a holiday-decorated blackboard. Back — a sleigh with a gift is being drawn toward a Christmas tree with white doves. Caption: "To a Special Teacher" and "Merry Christmas 1979."

White Satin, 3 1/4" diam.
350QX213-9, $3.50 ☐

New Home

A quaint painting of a snow-covered village, covered bridge, and ice skaters. Caption: "Christmas...when love fills the heart, when hearts look to home" and "1979."

Ecru Soft Sheen Satin, 3 1/4" diam.
350QX212-7, $3.50 ☐

Betsey Clark-Seventh Edition, PEANUTS, Spencer Sparrow

Joan Walsh Anglund, Winnie-the-Pooh™, Mary Hamilton

Night Before Christmas, Christmas Chickadees, Behold the Star

Property Ornaments

Betsey Clark — Seventh Edition

Front — Miss Clark's little children are sitting at home reading. Back — they are returning home from shopping with their tree-laden sled. This is the seventh ornament in the series. Caption: "Holiday fun times make memories to treasure. 1979."

White Satin, 3¼" diam.
350QX201-9, $3.50 ☐

PEANUTS® (Time to Trim)

Woodstock and his merry, green-capped flock are decorating the tree with the candy canes that SNOOPY is passing out to them. Caption: "Merry Christmas 1979."

White Satin, 3¼" diam.
350QX202-7, $3.50 ☐

Spencer Sparrow

Spencer swinging on a popcorn and cranberry garland, jauntily tips his hat. Caption: "Christmas time means decorating, spreading cheer and celebrating!" and "1979."

Ecru Soft-Sheen Satin, 3¼" diam.
350QX200-7, $3.50 ☐

Joan Walsh Anglund©

Front — the Anglund children are hanging their stockings on the fireplace. Back — little girl is opening her gift under the candlelit tree, while the little boy rides his new hobby horse. Caption: "The smallest pleasure is big enough to share. 1979."

White Satin, 3¼" diam.
350QX205-9, $3.50 ☐

Winnie-the-Pooh

Pooh's friends gather and deliver "Hunny" to a very happy bear. This is a Walt Disney design. Caption: "Merry Christmas 1979."

White Satin, 3¼" diam.
350QX206-7, $3.50 ☐

Mary Hamilton

An angelic choir sings to an audience of forest friends. Caption: "...and heaven and nature sing" and "1979."

Ecru Soft-Sheen Satin, 3¼" diam.
350QX254-7, $3.50 ☐

Decorative Ball Ornaments

Night Before Christmas

Front — this favorite Christmas poem is illustrated with Santa preparing to fill the "stockings hung by the chimney with care." Back — pictures Santa continuing on his journey and concluding lines of poem. Caption: "...I heard him exclaim, ere he drove out of sight, Happy Christmas to all, and to all a good night—C.C. Moore" and "1979."

White Satin, 3¼" diam.
350QX214-7, $3.50 ☐

Christmas Chickadees

A pair of chickadees enjoy the red berries of a holly branch. Two others frolic in the snow on a pine bough. Caption: "Beauty is a gift nature gives every day" and "Christmas 1979."

Gold Glass, 3¼" diam.
350QX204-7, $3.50 ☐

Behold the Star

The three wise men and shepherds with their flock follow the star to Bethlehem where the Child lies in a manger. Caption: "And the light was for all time"; "And the love was for all men."

White Satin, 3¼" diam.
350QX255-9, $3.50 ☐

Christmas Traditions

Homey Christmas traditions are exemplified in jar of candy, basket of fresh fruit, lantern with glowing candle, kitchen scales, wooden carved toy, and old mantle clock shown against a wood paneled wall. Caption: "The old may be replaced with new, traditions rearranged, but the wonder that is Christmas will never ever change. 1979."

Gold Glass, 3¼" diam.
350QX253-9, $3.50 ☐

Christmas Collage

Old-fashioned toys and the caption are highlighted on a dark brown and blue profusely decorated band reproduced from a photograph of a Schneeberg collage. Caption: "Season's Greetings" and "1979."

Gold Glass, 3¼" diam.
350QX257-9, $3.50 ☐

Christmas Traditions, Christmas Collage, Black Angel, Light of Christmas

Black Angel

Young adult angel wearing a red and white robe is shown in two scenes which utilized contemporary photographic effects to illustrate the radiance of the Christmas season. Caption: "Merry Christmas 1979."

Gold Glass, 3¼" diam.
350QX207-9, $3.50 ☐

The Light of Christmas

Reminiscent of Art Deco designs in stained glass, this red, orange, and green design encircles the caption on one side and, on the other, frames three lighted candles. Caption: "There's no light as bright as Christmas to adorn and warm the night. 1979."

Chrome Glass, 3¼" diam.
350QX256-7, $3.50 ☐

Holiday Highlights: Christmas Angel, Snowflake, Christmas Tree

Colors of Christmas: Words of Christmas, Wreath, Partridge, Star over Bethlehem

Holiday Highlights: Christmas Cheer, Love

A Matchless Christmas, Angel Delight

Holiday Highlights

Christmas Angel

Flying angel with elegantly "etched," long floral dress, feathery wings, and halo holds nosegay of flowers. A ribbon worn over the shoulder and falling to her side carries the caption: "Christmas 1979."

Acrylic, 4¼" wide
350QX300-7, $3.50 ☐

Snowflake

Exquisitely shaped snowflake has date "etched" in center hexagon. Caption: "1979."

Acrylic, 3½" diam.
350QX301-9, $3.50 ☐

Christmas Tree

A perfectly shaped, "etched" tree of leaves and flowers highlights a lone dove near the top. On the top in a halo effect is "1979." The date is stamped in silver foil. Caption: "1979."

Acrylic, 4½" tall
350QX302-7, $3.50 ☐

Christmas Cheer

A plump little bird with berries in its beak perches on a holly bough. Caption: "1979."

Acrylic, 3½" diam.
350QX303-9, $3.50 ☐

Love

Beribboned flowers border a heart containing a message stamped in silver foil flowing script. Caption: "Time of memories and dreams...Time of love. Christmas 1979."

Acrylic, 3½" tall
350QX304-7, $3.50 ☐

Colors of Christmas

Words of Christmas

Message forms a design in stained-glass look. The colors are red, green, and gold. Caption: "The message of Christmas is love."

Acrylic, 3¾" tall
350QX350-7, $3.50 ☐

Holiday Wreath

Wreath decorated with colorfully designed ornaments and topped with a red bow frames red year date. Caption: "1979."

Acrylic, 3½" tall
350QX353-9, $3.50 ☐

Partridge in a Pear Tree

A richly colored partridge surrounded by golden pears and green leaves is the center focus of this design. Caption: "1979."

Acrylic, 3¼" diam.
350QX351-9, $3.50 ☐

Star Over Bethlehem

Three shepherds and their flock behold the city of Bethlehem in the distance brilliantly illuminated by the "Star."

Acrylic, 3½" diam.
350QX352-7, $3.50 ☐

Little Trimmer Collection

Thimble Series — Mouse

First in the Thimble Series introduced in 1978, the popular Thimble Mouse was reissued in 1979. (See 1978 Collection for photograph and description.)

Handcrafted, 1¾" tall
300QX133-6, $3.00

Santa

Santa, introduced in 1978, was reissued in 1979. (See 1978 Collection.)

Handcrafted, 2¼" tall
300QX135-6, $3.00

A Matchless Christmas

A small white mouse has made a comfy bed in a half-opened matchbox. Wearing a red nightcap and lying on a white pillow with red stripes, he sleeps snugly under a blue-and-white checked blanket. This ornament clips onto the tree branch.

Handcrafted, 2½" long
400QX132-7, $4.00 ☐

Note: *The Angel, Matchless Christmas, and Santa also were packaged together as a trio of "Little Trimmers."*

Angel Delight

Little angel with white wings, golden halo, and light blue gown sails along in her walnut shell.

Handcrafted, 1¾" tall
300QX130-7, $3.00 ☐

Handcrafted Ornaments

Holiday Scrimshaw

Ivory angel wtih widespread wings and clasped hands has the look of scrimshaw carving. Caption: "Peace-Love-Joy 1979."

Handcrafted, 3½" tall
400QX152-7, $4.00 ☐

Christmas Heart

Two doves rotate through the center of this heart-shaped ornament. Design has the look of hand-carved wood, with raised floral motif highlighted by hand painting. Caption: "1979."

Handcrafted, 3½" tall
650QX140-7, $6.50 ☐

Christmas Eve Surprise

A wood-look shadow box reveals a three-dimensional scene of toy-laden Santa who is about to go down the chimney. Caption: "1979."

Handcrafted, 4¼" tall
650QX157-9, $6.50 ☐

Santa's Here

Santa is the center of attention as he twirls inside this snowflake. Caption: "1979."

Handcrafted, 4" diam.
500QX138-7, $5.00 ☐

Holiday Scrimshaw, Christmas Heart, Christmas Eve Surprise, Santa's Here

Downhill Run, The Drummer Boy, Outdoor Fun

A Christmas Treat, Skating Snowman, Christmas is for Children, Ready for Christmas

Raccoon

Mr. Raccoon on skates of real metal skated out of 1978 and into the 1979 Hallmark Keepsake Collection. This is a reissue. (See 1978 Annual Collection.)

Handcrafted, 2″ tall
650QX142-3, $6.50

The Downhill Run

Red capped squirrel and rabbit wearing blue scarf are having fun on a red toboggan making a fast downhill run.

Handcrafted, 3″ tall
650QX145-9, $6.50 ☐

The Drummer Boy

Standing in the snow near a fence and a tree is a drummer boy playing for a lamb and a duck.

Handcrafted, 3¼″ diam.
800QX143-9, $8.00 ☐

Outdoor Fun

Young girl on swing gently glides between two Christmas trees in snow scene.

Handcrafted, 3″ tall
800QX150-7, $8.00 ☐

A Christmas Treat

A teddy bear wearing red cap and jacket trimmed in white tries climbing a large candy cane which is designed to hook over a tree branch.

Handcrafted, 4¾″ tall
500QX134-7, $5.00 ☐

The Skating Snowman

Wearing a green-and-white, real cloth scarf, ice skates of real metal, and black top hat, this snowman cuts a fancy figure.

Handcrafted, 4¼″ tall
500QX139-9, $5.00 ☐

Christmas is for Children

Green bonneted little girl dressed in a red dress and red-and-white stockings holds a white kitten as she swings. All made in the look of hand carved wood.

Handcrafted, 4¼″ tall
500QX135-9, $5.00 ☐

Ready for Christmas

White birdhouse with a sparkling, snow-covered roof and green garland with a red bow over the door makes a cozy home for "Mr. and Mrs. Redbird."

Handcrafted, 3″ tall
650QX133-9,$6.50 ☐

Collectible Series

Carrousel — Second Edition

Second issue in the popular Carrousel Series has four angel musicians dressed in red, blue, deep rose, and green revolving on a red, blue, and green carrousel. Caption: "Christmas 1979" twice around the carrousel's top.

Handcrafted, 3½" tall
650QX146-7, $6.50 ☐

Thimble — Second Edition
A Christmas Salute

Soldier, with epaulets on the shoulders of his red jacket, wears blue trousers and thimble "hat." He salutes left-handed.

Handcrafted, 2¼" tall
300QX131-9, $3.00 ☐

SNOOPY and Friends - First Edition
Ice Hockey Holiday

SNOOPY and Woodstock play ice hockey on a frozen pond. Caption: "1979."

Handcrafted, 3¼" diam.
800QX141-9, $8.00 ☐

Here Comes Santa — First Edition
Santa's Motorcar

Santa is waving his hand as he drives into the holidays in a vintage motorcar. The car has the look of real cast metal and the wheels actually turn. The car is red trimmed in green, and the tires are black with golden spokes in the wheels. Santa's toy-filled bag is painted green and rests on the back of the car. Caption: "1979."

Handcrafted, 3½" tall
900QX155-9, $9.00 ☐

Bellringer — First Edition

Merry elf swings on the clapper of white porcelain bell decorated with fired on wreath decal. Rim of bell is hand painted in gold. Caption: "1979" in center of wreath.

Porcelain & Handcrafted, 4" tall
10QX147-9, $10.00 ☐

Collectible Series: Carrousel-Second Edition, Thimble-Second Edition

Collectible Series First Editions: Snoopy and Friends, Here Comes Santa, The Bellringer

Holiday Chimes

Reindeer Chimes

A reissue from 1978. (See 1978 Annual Collection.)

Chrome plate, 5½" tall
450QX320-3, $4.50

Star Chimes

Stars within stars twirl to create dancing reflections. Solid center star carries impressed year date. Caption: "1979."

Chrome Plate, 4" tall
450QX137-9, $4.50 ☐

Yarn and Fabric Ornaments

Sewn Trimmers

Four new sewn designs are added that feature quilting and stitched edges. Ranging from 4" to 5" tall, they were $2.00 each.

200QX340-7	*The Rocking Horse*	☐
200QX342-7	*Merry Santa*	☐
200QX341-9	*Stuffed Full Stocking*	☐
200QX343-9	*Angel Music*	☐

Yarn Ornaments

The four designs available in 1978 were offered again in 1979. (See 1978 Annual Collection for photograph and description.)

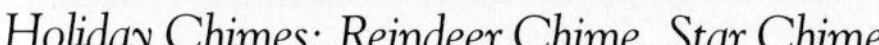

Holiday Chimes: Reindeer Chime, Star Chime

Sewn Ornaments: Rocking Horse, Merry Santa, Stuffed Full Stocking, Angel Music

THE 1980 COLLECTION

In 1980, Hallmark introduced seventy-six new ornament designs, eighteen more than the fifty-eight offered in 1979. Seven commemorative ball ornaments were inaugurated — Son, Daughter, Grandparents, Dad, Mother and Dad, Grandfather, and Baby's First Christmas for a black child. New properties included Jim Henson's MUPPETS™ and the drawing of Marty Links.™

Friendship, Mother, and First Christmas Together captioned ornaments were added to the acrylic line. Pastel colored, unbreakable "cameo" designs were introduced. Made of acrylic, they feature delicate, milk-white "cameo" reliefs on soft pastel backgrounds. The rims are chrome with a loop for hanging. Other new designs and formats in 1980 included frosted images (with the look of softly etched crystal), a flocked ornament, and a pressed tin ornament.

Two new collectible series were issued: Frosty Friends (an Eskimo and a polar bear on a dated icecube) and the first Norman Rockwell cameo ornament. Two special edition ornaments also made their first appearance: Checking It Twice (a very detailed Santa checking his list) and Heavenly Minstrel (a beautiful blue angel).

By 1980, marketing surveys indicated that 55 percent of all Hallmark ornament purchases were made by collectors adding to their collections.

Baby's First Christmas: Satin Ball, Satin Ball (Black Baby), Handcrafted

Commemoratives

Baby's First Christmas

Santa with his bag on his back is talking to a baby who is in a brass baby bed. Caption: "Baby's First Christmas, 1980."

White Satin, 3¼" diam.
400QX200-1, $4.00 ☐

Black Baby's First Christmas

Another Hallmark first, a black baby dressed in a nightie sits by a decorated Christmas tree that holds nested birds in its branches. Toys surround the tree. Caption: "Baby's First Christmas, 1980."

White Satin, 3¼" diam.
400QX229-4, $4.00 ☐

Baby's First Christmas

A wood-look shadow box in the shape of a Christmas tree has five compartments. The compartments hold a silver cup with "Baby" on it, a rubber duck, alphabet blocks, a white ball with a blue star on it, four wood-look rings in red, yellow, and green, and a teddy bear. Caption: "Baby's First Christmas" and "1980."

Handcrafted, 3 57/64" tall
12QX156-1, $12.00 ☐

Grandson

Front — a jolly snowman rides a sled pulled by raccoons. Back — the snowman adds a candy cane to a decorated tree. Caption: "Grandsons and Christmas are joys that go together. Christmas 1980."

White Satin, 3¼" diam.
400QX201-4, $4.00 ☐

Granddaughter

Little girl, nestled under a patchwork quilt in a brass bed, dreams of sweets and toys. Caption: "A Granddaughter is a dream fulfilled, a treasure to hold dear, a joy to warmly cherish, a comfort through the year. Christmas 1980."

Ecru Soft-Sheen Satin, 3¼" diam.
400QX202-1, $4.00 ☐

Son

Nostalgic scene of favorite boys' toys. Caption: "A son is...a maker of memories, a source of pride...A son is love. Christmas 1980."

Gold Glass, 3¼" diam.
400QX211-4, $4.00 ☐

Daughter

This is the first year of the Daughter ornament. Front — white kitten naps next to potted flowers and plants. Back — kitten plays with ornaments hanging on a potted plant. Caption: "A Daughter is the sweetest gift a lifetime can provide. Christmas 1980."

White Glass, 3¼" diam.
400QX212-1, $4.00 ☐

Grandson, Granddaughter, Son, Daughter

Dad, Mother, Mother and Dad

Grandmother, Grandfather, Grandparents

Dad

Front — the word "DAD" is printed on red plaid background. Back — red oval containing caption. Caption: "A Dad is always caring, always sharing, always giving of his love. Christmas 1980."

Gold Glass, 3¼" diam.
400QX214-1, $4.00 ☐

Mother

Large poinsettias and other Christmas flowers ring ornament and frame caption. Caption: "A Mother has the special gift of giving of herself. Christmas 1980."

White Satin, 3¼" diam.
400QX203-4, $4.00 ☐

Mother and Dad

Against a light green background, darker green script printing and sprays of holly and red berries circle the ornament. Caption: "When homes are decked with holly and hearts are feeling glad, it's a wonderful time to remember a wonderful Mother and Dad. Christmas 1980."

White Glass, 3¼" diam.
400QX230-1, $4.00 ☐

Grandmother

Flowers, birds, and animals frame the caption and date. Caption: "Love and joy and comfort and cheer are gifts a Grandmother gives all year. Christmas 1980."

White Glass, 3¼" diam.
400QX204-1, $4.00 ☐

Grandfather

Two snow scenes, one of an old covered bridge, and the other of an idle wagon in a barnyard are pictured. Caption: "A Grandfather is...strong in his wisdom, gentle in his love. Christmas 1980."

White Glass, 3¼" diam.
400QX231-4, $4.00 ☐

Grandparents

Large home by wooded pond reproduced from Currier & Ives print, "Early Winter." Caption: "Grandparents have beautiful ways of giving, of helping, of teaching...especially of loving. 1980."

Gold Glass, 3¼" diam.
400QX213-4, $4.00 ☐

25th Christmas Together, First Christmas Together, Christmas Love

Friendship, Christmas at Home, Teacher

Love, Beauty of Friendship, First Christmas Together, Mother

25th Christmas Together

Applique-style garlands, bells, and ribbons frame the captions. Caption: "The good times of the present blend with memories of the past to make each Christmas season even dearer than the last. 25th Christmas Together. 1980."

White Glass, 3¼" diam.
400QX206-1, $4.00 ☐

First Christmas Together

A couple takes a moonlight sleighride in the snow. Caption: "First Christmas Together. Christmas is a love story written in our hearts. 1980."

White Glass, 3¼" diam.
400QX205-4, $4.00 ☐

Christmas Love

This ornament is a reproduction of a Bob Schneeberg collage. Motif in delicate, soft pastels is of hearts trimmed in beads and pearls, a large snowflake, and "LOVE" in ornate lettering. Caption: "Love at Christmas...happy moments spent together, memories to be shared forever. Christmas 1980."

White Glass, 3¼" diam.
400QX207-4, $4.00 ☐

Friendship

White lace, red ribbons, and flowers on a muted green background. Caption: "Hold Christmas ever in your heart — For its meaning never ends; Its spirit is the warmth and joy of remembering friends. Christmas 1980."

White Glass, 3¼" diam.
400QX208-1, $4.00 ☐

Christmas at Home

Yule decorated hearth and brightly burning logs personify the comfort and warmth of home. Caption: "A Home that's filled with Christmas Glows with the joyful light Of the special warmth and happiness That makes the season bright. Christmas 1980."

Gold Glass, 3¼" diam.
400QX210-1, $4.00 ☐

Teacher

Front — warmly dressed kitten bearing a gift is walking to school. Back — he is placing the gift on the teacher's desk. A blackboard has a special message for teacher. Caption: "Merry Christmas, Teacher. Christmas 1980."

White Satin, 3¼" diam.
400QX209-4, $4.00 ☐

Betsey Clark-Eighth Edition, Betsey Clark, Betsey Clark's Christmas

Love

Lettering of caption appears cut and etched, with the word "LOVE" enhanced by silver foil stamping. Large snowflake in the center of the "O" is the focal point of the ornament. Caption: "Where there is love, there is the spirit of Christmas. 1980."

Acrylic, 4" tall
400QX302-1, $4.00 ☐

Beauty of Friendship

Clear, disk-shaped ornament has floral garland border and center caption and date stamped in silver foil. Caption: "Friendship brings beauty to our days, joy to our world. Christmas 1980."

Acrylic, 3¼" diam.
400QX303-4, $4.00 ☐

First Christmas Together

Heart-shaped, with floral and ribbon border, has caption and date stamped in silver foil. Caption: "First Christmas Together 1980."

Acrylic, 3½" tall
400QX305-4, $4.00 ☐

Mother

Heart with ribbon-tied floral border has silver foil stamped caption and date. Caption: "Mother is another word for Love. Christmas 1980."

Acrylic, 3½" tall
400QX304-1, $4.00 ☐

Property Ornaments

Betsey Clark — Eighth Edition

Betsey Clark's charming children are sledding past a sign in the snow announcing "Christmas 1980." This is the eighth dated design in the Betsey Clark Series. Caption: "It's joy-in-the-air time, love everywhere time, good-fun-to-share time, it's Christmas. Christmas 1980."

White Glass, 3¼" diam.
400QX215-4, $4.00 ☐

Betsey Clark

On a soft blue background, a Betsey Clark angel is kneeling in prayer with clasped hands. A banner beneath her carries the date. The angel is surrounded by embossed stars and a holly border, as is the caption on the back of the ornament. Caption: "Love came down at Christmas, Love all lovely, Love divine: Love was born at Christmas, Star and Angels gave the sign" and "Christmas 1980."

Light Blue Cameo, 3⅜" diam.
650QX307-4, $6.50 ☐

Betsey Clark's Christmas

A red shadow box trimmed in white band with red ribbon features Betsey Clark girl in a three-dimensional snowscene. Caption: "1980."

Handcrafted, 4" tall
750QX149-4, $7.50 ☐

PEANUTS®
SNOOPY sings as Woodstock and his friends reenact verses from traditional Christmas carol. Caption: "Four colly birds...three French hens...and a partridge in a pear tree. Christmas 1980."

White Satin, 3¼" diam.
400QX216-1, $4.00 □

Joan Walsh Anglund©
The Anglund children are having an ice skating holiday. Caption: "Each and every bright December brings the best times to remember. Christmas 1980."

White Satin, 3¼" diam.
400QX217-4, $4.00 □

DISNEY
Front — Mickey and Minnie Mouse are ice skating. Back — Mickey plays Santa as he approaches a house to make a delivery. Caption: "Merry Christmas 1980."

White Satin, 3¼" diam.
400QX218-1, $4.00 □

Mary Hamilton
Two charming children are reflected in the glow of an old-fashioned candlelit Christmas tree. Caption: "Christmas — the warmest, brightest season of all. Christmas 1980."

Gold Glass, 3¼" diam.
400QX219-4, $4.00 □

MUPPETS™
Front — KERMIT™ waves a greeting. Back — MUPPETS™ are merrily caroling. This design is the first appearance of Jim Hensen's MUPPETS™ as a Hallmark Keepsake Ornament. Caption: "Merry Christmas 1980."

White Satin, 3¼" diam.
400QX220-1, $4.00 □

Marty Links™
Little girl directs as a little boy and animals carol in the snow. Caption: "We wish you a Merry Christmas and a Happy New Year. Christmas 1980."

White Satin, 3¼" diam.
400QX221-4, $4.00 □

Decorative Ball Ornaments

Christmas Choir
Front — snowscene of country church. Back — three darling black children dressed in choir robes are singing the message of Christmas. One is so small she stands on a stool. Caption: "Go tell it on the mountain...Jesus Christ is born! Christmas 1980."

Gold Glass, 3¼" diam.
400QX228-1, $4.00 □

PEANUTS®, Joan Walsh Anglund,© DISNEY

Mary Hamilton, Muppets™, Marty Links™

Christmas Choir, Nativity, Christmas Time

Santa's Workshop, Happy Christmas, Jolly Santa, Christmas Cardinals

Nativity
Animals and birds gather beside small children kneeling in prayer at the manger of the Christ Child. Caption: "Silent night...holy night...Christmas 1980."

Gold Glass, 3¼" diam.
400QX225-4, $4.00 ☐

Christmas Time
Front — a stagecoach rolling along in the snow toward timbered inn. Back — holly-sprigged top hat and steaming mug of coffee. Caption: "These are the days of merry-making, get-togethers, journey-taking, moments of delight and love that last in memory. Christmas 1980."

Ecru Soft-Sheen Satin, 3¼" diam.
400QX226-1, $4.00 ☐

Santa's Workshop
Front — merry Santa has added a warm scarf to his traditional costume. Back — Santa checking his list at his North Pole workshop. Caption: "What merriment is all around when dear old Santa comes to town. Christmas 1980."

White Satin, 3¼" diam.
400QX223-4, $4.00 ☐

Happy Christmas
Front — a Koala bear waters a potted tree. Back — tree has magically grown into "pear tree" of Christmas song with small bird perched at top. Caption: "Tis the season when hearts are glowing, love is growing, and happiness rounds out the year! Christmas 1980."

Ecru Soft-Sheen Satin, 3¼" diam.
400QX222-1, $4.00 ☐

Jolly Santa
Ice skating Santa and reindeer spell out the season's greetings. Caption: "Merry Christmas. Christmas 1980."

White Glass, 3¼" diam.
400QX227-4, $4.00 ☐

Christmas Cardinals
Two cardinals perch on berry-laden branches of holly. Caption: "Nature at Christmas...a wonderland of wintry art. Christmas 1980."

White Glass, 3¼" diam.
400QX224-1, $4.00 ☐

Holiday Highlights: Three Wisemen, Wreath

Colors of Christmas: Joy

Holiday Highlights

Three Wise Men

Three Wise Men follow the star to Bethlehem. Intricate detail shows their regal attire and the gifts they are bearing. Created with the look of hand-cut, etched crystal. Caption: "Christmas 1980."

Acrylic, 4" tall
400QX300-1, $4.00 ☐

Wreath

Wreath topped with luxurious bow features leaves and holly in etched effect. Clear fruit and berries form pleasing contrast. Date is stamped in silver foil on clear center. Caption: "1980."

Acrylic, 3¼" diam.
400QX301-4, $4.00 ☐

Colors of Christmas

Joy

Fashioned in rich colors with the look of leaded stained glass, the ornament is molded to spell "JOY," with year date on ribbon scroll over the "O". Caption: "Joy 1980."

Acrylic, 4" tall
400QX350-1, $4.00 ☐

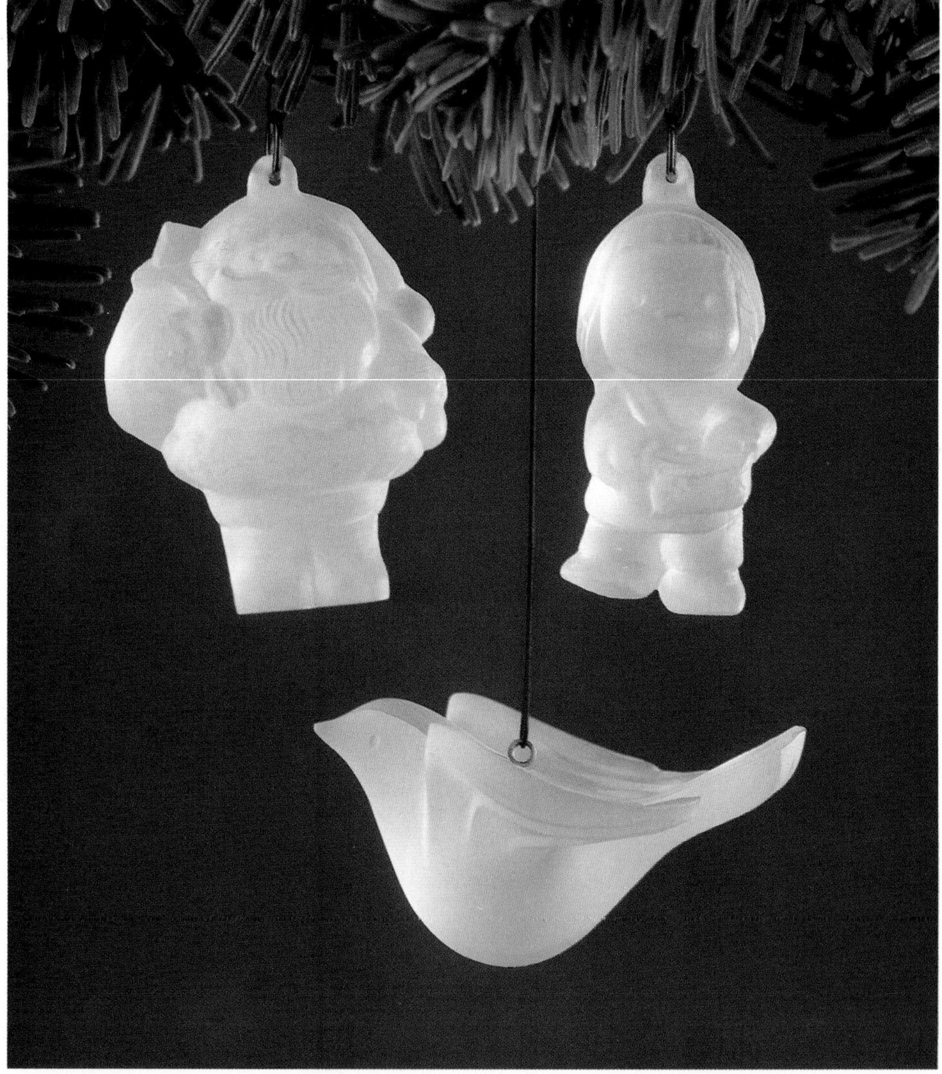

Frosted Images: Santa, Drummer Boy, Dove

Little Trimmers: Clothespin Soldier, Christmas Teddy, Merry Redbird, Swinging on a Star, Christmas Owl

Frosted Images

Three new frosted images were new introductions in the 1980 collection of Hallmark Keepsake Ornaments. The naturalistically shaped acrylic ornaments have the appearance of delicate, frosted crystal. They range in size from 1⅞" to 2¼" tall and were $4.00 each.

400QX309-4 Drummer Boy ☐
400QX310-1 Santa ☐
400QX308-1 Dove ☐

Little Trimmers

Clothespin Soldier

Proud little soldier in the style of a clothespin is dressed in hand-painted blue trousers, red jacket with white trim, and a red hat.

Handcrafted, 2 15/16" tall
350QX134-1, $3.50 ☐

Christmas Teddy

Small brown teddy bear has a smile painted on his face, black painted outline around the ears and paws, and a red heart painted on his chest. He is made from dough-look material.

Handcrafted, 1¼" tall
250QX135-4, $2.50 ☐

Merry Redbird

In a new format, merry redbird wears softly flocked "feathers" and carries a sprig of holly in his yellow bill.

Handcrafted-Flocked, 1 27/32" long
350QX160-1, $3.50 ☐

Swingin' on a Star

Tiny white mouse in a red-and-green striped cap with a brass bell is swinging on a brass star.

Handcrafted, 2 5/32" tall
400QX130-1, $4.00 ☐

Christmas Owl

A Christmas owl cutie wearing a "Santa" cap clutches holly and berries in his beak as he perches on a snow-covered tree stump.

Handcrafted, 1 27/32" tall
400QX131-4, $4.00 ☐

Thimble Series — A Christmas Salute

This is a reissue of the second design in the Thimble Series; it was introduced in 1979. (See 1979 Annual Collection.)

Handcrafted, 2¼" tall
400QX131-9, $4.00

Handcrafted Ornaments

The Snowflake Swing
An angel clad in green swings merrily from a dainty star molded of clear acrylic.

Handcrafted, 3″ tall
400QX133-4, $4.00 ☐

Santa 1980
Snow-capped chimney represents the "1" in 1980, and Santa is seen making an entrance to mouse's house, below. Small mouse with empty stocking awaits Santa's visit. Ornament is fashioned in "dough-look" material.

Handcrafted, 4 5/32″ tall
550QX146-1, $5.50 ☐

Drummer Boy
The drummer boy in bread-dough design has textured hair and is dressed in green with brown sandals and stocking cap. His red drum is accented in gold. Caption: "1980."

Handcrafted, 3 3/64″ tall
550QX147-4, $5.50 ☐

Christmas Is for Children
This little girl in swing with real motion is reissue of popular model introduced in 1979. (See 1979 Annual Collection.)

Handcrafted, 4¼″ tall
550QX135-9, $5.50

A Christmas Treat
The teddy climbing a large candy cane is reissue of a favorite in the 1979 line. (See 1979 Annual Collection.)

Handcrafted, 4¾″ tall
550QX134-7, $5.50

Skating Snowman
Wearing a top hat, a real cloth scarf, and metal skates, appealing snowman is a 1979 reissue. (See 1979 Annual Collection.)

Handcrafted, 4¼″ tall
550QX139-9, $5.50

A Heavenly Nap
An angel dressed in blue is taking a nap on a crescent-shaped moon. There must be a man in the moon, for this frosted acrylic moon seems to be fast asleep in a nightcap with a gold star tassel.

Handcrafted, 3½″ tall
650QX139-4, $6.50 ☐

Snowflake Swing, Santa 1980, Drummer Boy

A Heavenly Nap, Heavenly Sounds, Caroling Bear, Santa's Flight

The Animal's Christmas, A Spot of Christmas Cheer, Elfin Antics, A Christmas Vigil

Heavenly Sounds

Angels dressed in pink and blue produce "heavenly sounds" by ringing a gold metal bell. They twirl about in the center of a wood-look pink ring decorated with green scrolls. Caption: "1980."

Handcrafted, $3\frac{30}{64}$" tall
750QX152-1, $7.50 ☐

Caroling Bear

A happy brown bear wearing a green-and-red striped scarf is singing a duet with a red bird perched on his arm. His green songbook carries the caption and date. Caption: "Carols 1980."

Handcrafted, $3\frac{7}{33}$" tall
750QX140-1, $7.50 ☐

Santa's Flight

Santa gives up the sleigh and reindeer to make Christmas deliveries in a dirigible of pressed tin. The white dirigible, decorated in blue and gold, is festooned with a green garland tied in red ribbon. Santa rides in the strawlike tin basket. The propeller actually twirls around! Caption: "Merry Christmas 1980."

Pressed Tin, 4" tall
550QX138-1, $5.50 ☐

The Animals' Christmas

A brown rabbit and a brown bird are decorating a snow-sprinkled Christmas tree.

Handcrafted, $2\frac{37}{64}$" tall
800QX150-1, $8.00 ☐

A Spot of Christmas Cheer

Inside a plump teapot, a chipmunk busily trims a Christmas tree. On the outside there is a window with shutters and windowed door with a golden doorknob and 1980 "house number." Green garland with perky red bow gracefully decorates this small "home." Caption: "1980."

Handcrafted, $2\frac{47}{64}$" tall
800QX153-4, $8.00 ☐

Elfin Antics

Dressed in holiday colors, acrobatic elves are tumbling down from the Christmas tree branch and right into Christmas. The bottom elf is ringing a gold metal bell.

Handcrafted, $4\frac{9}{16}$" tall
900QX142-1, $9.00 ☐

A Christmas Vigil

Pajama-clad little boy and his dog peek out the bedroom window just in time to glimpse Santa and his reindeer flying through the sky on Christmas Eve.

Handcrafted, $3\frac{13}{16}$" tall
900QX144-1, $9.00 ☐

Special Editions: A Heavenly Minstrel, Checking It Twice

Special Editions

Heavenly Minstrel

A beautiful old world angel with widespread wings is wearing a softly flowing blue dress, beige stole trimmed in gold, and turquoise ribbon in her hair. She is playing a celestial lute. Intricate details of this design make it exceptionally appealing.

Handcrafted, $6\frac{1}{4}$" tall
15QX156-7, $15.00 ☐

Checking It Twice

An elfin Santa with pointed ears is "checking his list" with real names printed on it. He is wearing spectacles of real metal, green elf-type shoes, red-and-white striped stockings, and suspendered red pants that end just below the knee. A ring of keys is caught in his belt loop.

Handcrafted, $5\frac{15}{16}$" tall
20QX158-4, $20.00 ☐

Holiday Chimes

Snowflake Chimes

Three stamped snowflakes revolve sparkling and chiming as they hang suspended from a fourth snowflake.

Chrome Plate, 1 59/64" diam.
550QX165-4, $5.50 ☐

Reindeer Chimes

Three reindeer "prance" from snowflake creating soft chimes and twinkling reflections. (Reissue from 1978 Annual Collection.)

Chrome Plate, 5½" tall
550QX320-3, $5.50

Santa Mobile

Santa with his sleigh and reindeer soar over three homes with smoking chimneys.

Chrome Plate, 3 57/64" tall
550QX136-1, $5.50 ☐

Collectible Series

Norman Rockwell — First Edition "Santa's Visitors"

Norman Rockwell's famous "Santa's Visitors" is reproduced in delicate white relief on a soft green background. This lovely collectible is sought by collectors of Norman Rockwell items as well as Christmas ornament collectors. Caption: "Santa's Visitors. The Norman Rockwell Collection, Christmas 1980."

Light Green Cameo, 3⅜" diam.
650QX306-1, $6.50 ☐

Frosty Friends — First Edition A Cool Yule

Sweet little Eskimo and polar bear friend are reading books with snowflakes on the covers while sitting on an icecube made of clear acrylic. The icecube is etched with the caption. This is the first issue in the Eskimo and Friend Series. Caption: "Merry Christmas 1980."

Handcrafted, 2 63/64" tall
650QX137-4, $6.50 ☐

SNOOPY and Friends — Second Edition SNOOPY Ski Holiday

The second design in this series reveals SNOOPY and Woodstock on a ski holiday. SNOOPY, wearing a red-and-green stocking cap, executes a dashing slalom, while just ahead of him Woodstock rides the slopes in SNOOPY's feeding bowl. Caption: "1980." and "SNOOPY."

Handcrafted, 3¼" diam.
900QX154-1, $9.00 ☐

Holiday Chimes: Santa Mobile, Snowflake Chime

New Collectible Series: Norman Rockwell-First Edition, Frosty Friends-First Edition

Collectible Series: Snoopy and Friends, Carrousel, Thimble

Collectible Series: Here Comes Santa, The Bellringer

Yarn Ornaments: Angel, Santa, Snowman, Soldier

Carrousel — Third Edition
Merry Carrousel

Santa and his reindeer are making their "rounds" on the carrousel design for 1980. The carrousel has bands of dots, circles, and flowers in red, white, green, and gold. The caption is on the top. This is the third in a very pretty and popular series. Caption: "Christmas 1980."

Handcrafted, 3⅛" tall
750QX141-4, $7.50 ☐

Thimble — Third Edition
Thimble Elf

Playful elf dressed in red and green swings on a thimble "bell" that hangs from a golden rope. This is third design in the Thimble Series.

Handcrafted, 2 31/32" tall
400QX132-1, $4.00 ☐

Here Comes Santa — Second Edition
Santa's Express

Santa steams into Christmas 1980 in an old-fashioned locomotive. In the look of iron, the locomotive is red and black trimmed in gold. The wheels actually turn. Santa the engineer waves from the cab. This is the second design in this collectible series. Caption: "1980."

Handcrafted, 3" tall
12QX143-4, $12.00 ☐

The Bellringers — Second Edition

Two blue gowned angels, suspended from red ribbon streamers at the top of the bell, circle and ring the white porcelain with star "clappers" they are holding. This is number two in the Bellringer series. Caption: "1980" in center of gold, red, and green garland.

Porcelain & Handcrafted, 2 7/64" tall
15QX157-4, $15.00 ☐

Yarn and Fabric Ornaments

Yarn Ornaments

Four exquisitely detailed yarn ornaments with accents of lace and felt were introduced in 1980. These new offerings were all 5" tall and priced at $3.00.

300QX161-4 *Santa* ☐
300QX162-1 *Angel* ☐
300QX163-4 *Snowman* ☐
300QX164-1 *Soldier* ☐

Sewn Trimmers

The four versatile family favorites in the 1979 line were reissued in 1980. (See 1979 Annual Collection for photograph and description.)

THE 1981 COLLECTION

Two commemorative ball ornaments were introduced in 1981 for Godchild and 50 Years Together. In addition, new Baby's First Christmas ball ornaments designed specifically for a boy and a girl were added to the line.

Photo holder ornaments were also introduced this year, and a wooden ornament (Drummer Boy) with movable arms and legs was a distinctive addition to the line. Plush, "stuffed animal" ornaments were first seen this year, and the first edition of the instantly popular handcrafted Rocking Horse series made its debut.

Commemoratives

Baby's First Christmas — Girl

Design in pink and white pictures a baby girl holding a teddy bear. They are centered in a delicate floral ring. Floral border circles ornament to frame caption and scene of toys and gifts. Caption: "Baby's First Christmas 1981" and "There's nothing like a baby girl to cheer and brighten all the world at Christmas."

White Satin, 3 1/4" diam.
450QX600-2, $4.50 ☐

Baby's First Christmas — Boy

A baby boy holding a stuffed animal is in a circled frame of snowflakes that continue around the ornament. Toys and gifts border the soft blue ornament. Caption: "Baby's First Christmas 1981" and "There's nothing like a baby boy to bring a world of special joy at Christmas."

White Satin, 3 1/4" diam.
450QX601-5, $4.50 ☐

Baby's First Christmas — Black

Front — a happy black baby rests on green gingham cushions with his teddy bear and other toys. Back — the baby plays peekaboo under his comforter. Caption: "Baby's First Christmas 1981" and "A baby is a gift of joy, a gift of love at Christmas."

Ecru Soft-Sheen Satin, 3 1/4" diam.
450QX602-2, $4.50 ☐

Baby's First Christmas

A green wreath decorated with a red bow, baby shoes, rattle, bells, blocks that spell "BABY," frames photograph opening. Back — design repeat and caption in gold and white. Caption: "A Baby is the nicest gift of all" and "Baby's First Christmas 1981."

Acrylic, 4" diam.
550QX516-2, $5.50 ☐

Baby's First Christmas

Front — cameo design on soft green background is of a large, gift-wrapped box, a rocking horse on wheels, blocks, stuffed animal, and toys. Back — caption circled with raised design of ribbon and lace. Caption: "Baby's First Christmas 1981" and "A baby adds a special joy to all the joys of Christmas."

Light Green Cameo, 3 3/8" diam.
850QX513-5, $8.50 ☐

Baby's First Christmas

Baby is tucked under captioned, fabric blanket in an old-fashioned baby carriage designed in the look of wicker. The wheels actually roll and the top of the carriage is festooned with red ribbon and bow. Caption: "Baby's First Christmas, 1981" printed on fabric blanket.

Handcrafted, 3 3/4" long
1300QX440-2, $13.00 ☐

Godchild

An angel and his puppy, floating on a cloud, are gathering stars from the sky and placing them in a bag. Background is blue. This is the first issue of this commemorative. Caption: "For a special Godchild" and "Christmas 1981."

White Satin, 3 1/4" diam.
450QX603-5, $4.50 ☐

Grandson

Santa and a reindeer are busy making and painting toys in his workshop. Caption: "A Grandson makes the 'Holly Days' extra bright and jolly days" and "Christmas 1981."

White Satin, 3 1/4" diam.
450QX604-2, $4.50 ☐

Granddaughter

Front — a plump white rocking horse with red, white, and blue ruffled and ribboned saddle is on a yellow background framed in a narrow red border design with blue nosegays at each side. Back — toys and the caption framed in border motif. Caption: "A Granddaughter adds a magical touch to the beauty and joy of Christmas" and "1981."

White Satin, 3 1/4" diam.
450QX605-5, $4.50 ☐

Daughter

Geometric design of "wallpaper" centered with pink flowers forms background of Christmas scene showing a kitten napping in a wicker chair, a doll, gifts, candy-filled jars, basket of flowers, and lighted candles. Caption: "A Daughter fills each day with joy by filling hearts with love" and "Christmas 1981."

Ecru Soft-Sheen Satin, 3 1/4" diam.
450QX607-5, $4.50 ☐

Son

Christmas tree, Santa, and a variety of toys are shown in multicolored squares. Caption: "A son puts the merry in Christmas" and "Christmas 1981."

White Satin, 3 1/4" diam.
450QX606-2, $4.50 ☐

Mother

Red roses and Christmas greenery surround the caption and date. Caption: "In a Mother's heart there is love...the very heart of Christmas." and "Christmas 1981."

White Satin, 3 1/4" diam.
450QX608-2, $4.50 ☐

Father

A beautiful male deer pausing briefly in a blue frozen forest. Caption: "Life changes season to season, year to year...but a Father's love is for always" and "Christmas 1981."

White Satin, 3 1/4" diam.
450QX609-5, $4.50 ☐

Mother and Dad

Front — white heart and red-lettered caption against background of holly and poinsettias on dark green. Back — Christmas message framed in holly and poinsettias. Caption: "For Mother and Dad, Christmas 1981" and "The wonderful meaning of Christmas is found in the circle of family love."

Ecru Soft-Sheen Satin, 3 1/4" diam.
450QX700-2, $4.50 ☐

Baby's First Christmas: For Girls, Boys and for Black Babies

Baby's First Christmas: Photoholder, Cameo, Handcrafted

Godchild, Grandson, Granddaughter, Daughter, Son

Mother, Father, Mother and Dad

Friendship
The caption is bordered by a harvest of fruit and flowers in shades of red and green. Caption: "The beauty of friendship never ends" and "Christmas 1981."

White Satin, 3¼" diam.
450QX704-2, $4.50 ☐

The Gift of Love
On a rich, deep blue background, red roses and holly leaves outlined in gold frame the gold-printed date and caption. Caption: "Love is a precious gift, priceless and perfect, cherished above all life's treasures" and "Christmas 1981."

Gold Glass, 3¼" diam.
450QX705-5, $4.50 ☐

Home
A lovely Victorian village scene with Christmas trees, gabled homes, and snow. Caption: "Christmas 1981" and "Love in the home puts joy in the heart."

White Satin, 3¼" diam.
450QX709-5, $4.50 ☐

Teacher
Red background and a red, green, blue, and white stocking filled with red apples for teacher. Caption: "For a special teacher, Christmas 1981."

White Satin, 3¼" diam.
450QX800-2, $4.50 ☐

Grandfather
The caption in red and gold is bordered by sprays of holly on a deep brown background. Caption: "Grandfather holds a special place in the heart" and "Christmas 1981."

Gold Glass, 3¼" diam.
450QX701-5, $4.50 ☐

Grandmother
Beige background with lacy border and poinsettias. Caption: "A Grandmother is so loving and dear at Christmas and throughout the year" and "Christmas 1981."

Ecru Soft-Sheen Satin, 3¼" diam.
450QX702-2, $4.50 ☐

Grandparents
A holly-sprigged basket filled with fruit, a jar of candy canes, Christmas ball ornaments, poinsettias, and a gift. Caption: "Grandparents give the gift of love at Christmas and all year 'round" and "1981."

White Glass, 3¼" diam.
450QX703-5, $4.50 ☐

Friendship, Gift of Love, Home, Teacher

Grandfather, Grandmother, Grandparents

First Christmas Together
Couple dressed in the style of the 1800s are ice skating against a red background sprinkled with golden snow-flakes. Hearts, poinsettias, blossoms, and holly in red, blue, and white band the ornament and frame heart shape enclosing caption on the back. Caption: "First Christmas Together 1981" and "Christmas...the season for sharing the spirit of Love.

Chrome Glass, 3¼" diam.
450QX706-2, $4.50 ☐

25th Christmas Together
White heart, white wedding bell, and white doves on green leaved and red floral background with red ribbons and bows. Caption: "25 Years Together, Christmas 1981" and "Christmas season of the heart, time of sweet remembrance."

White Glass, 3¼" diam.
450QX707-5, $4.50 ☐

50th Christmas
Brilliant red poinsettias, holly, and berries surround the captions on the front and back panels of this design. Caption: "Fifty Years Together, Christmas 1981" and "A treasure of memories is a very special happiness."

Gold Glass, 3¼" diam.
450QX708-2, $4.50 ☐

Love
A heart with the caption in its center has a wide border of etched holly and poinsettias. Caption is stamped with silver foil. Caption: "Love...the nicest gift of all. Christmas 1981."

Clear Acrylic, 3½" tall
550QX502-2, $5.50 ☐

Friendship
Perky squirrel holding a songbook sings a Christmas duet with his feathered friend. The caption curves across the top and is stamped with silver foil. Caption: "Friends put the "Merry" in Christmas" and "1981."

Clear Acrylic, 3¼" diam.
550QX503-5, $5.50 ☐

First Christmas Together
Quatrefoil ornament has the caption etched on the face and stamped with gold foil. Caption: "First Christmas Together 1981."

Clear Acrylic, 3" tall
550QX505-5, $5.50 ☐

First Christmas, Twenty-Fifth Christmas, Fiftieth Christmas

Love, Friendship, First Christmas, Twenty-Fifth Christmas

25th Christmas Together
Two molded wedding bells with frosted border designs are caught and tied with large ribbon bow and holly. The caption is etched on the forward bell and stamped in silver foil. Caption: "25 Years Together, Christmas 1981."

Clear Acrylic, 4½" tall
550QX504-2, $5.50 ☐

Property Ornaments

Betsey Clark

The background in soft blue is edged with raised border of ribbons and flowers. The cameo is of a little girl petting a small fawn. Caption: "Christmas, when hearts reach out to give and receive the gentle gifts of love" and "1981."

Soft Blue Cameo, 3⅜" diam.
850QX512-2, $8.50 ☐

Betsey Clark

A Betsey Clark girl dressed in red and white and an inquisitive fawn are standing in the snow looking at a snow-covered tree topped with a yellow star.

Handcrafted, 3 9/32" tall
900QX423-5, $9.00 ☐

Betsey Clark — Ninth Edition

Front — lace-bordered circle around scene of a little girl leaving a gift for her small friend who is standing in the doorway of her home. Back — the little girl pulls a gift-filled sleigh as she continues on her way delivering gifts. Background is in red, white, and blue patchwork. Ninth design in this collectible series. Caption: "Christmas 1981" and "The greatest joy of Christmas day comes from the joy we give away."

White Glass, 3¼" diam.
450QX802-2, $4.50 ☐

MUPPETS™

Front — KERMIT™, dressed as Santa with a bag of toys, is on his way down the chimney. Back — MISS PIGGY™, elegantly gowned, lounges in front of fireplace awaiting Santa's visit. Her empty "stocking" is a high-heeled, fur-trimmed red boot. Caption: "Let's hear it for Christmas" and "Let's hear it for Santa" and "1981."

White Satin, 3¼" diam.
450QX807-5, $4.50 ☐

KERMIT the FROG™

KERMIT™ dons a red-and-white cap for a coasting adventure on his realistic sled.

Handcrafted, 3 11/32" long
900QX424-2, $9.00 ☐

THE DIVINE MISS PIGGY™

MISS PIGGY™ poses as an angel with a brass halo and white wings. She is dressed in an aqua evening gown, lavender shoes, long gloves, and her trademark "diamond" ring is on her pinkie.

Handcrafted, 4" long
1200QX425-5, $12.00 ☐

Betsey Clark Cameo, Handcrafted, Betsey Clark - Ninth Edition

MUPPETS™, KERMIT the FROG™, THE DIVINE MISS PIGGY™

Mary Hamilton, Marty Links

PEANUTS™, Joan Walsh Anglund,© DISNEY

Mary Hamilton

Little angels are decorating, reading, napping, and playing musical instruments on a heavenly blue background. Caption: "Christmas 1981" and "Christmas decorates the world with wonder."

Gold Glass, 3¼″ diam.
450QX806-2, $4.50 ☐

Marty Links

Front — two Marty Links children carrying a very large candy cane are followed by their hungry puppy. Back — laughing little girl holds mistletoe over her head. Caption: "Christmas 1981" and "Happy hearts and good times go hand in hand at Christmas."

White Satin, 3¼″ diam.
450QX808-2, $4.50 ☐

PEANUTS™

SNOOPY, Woodstock, and his flock sing merrily as they deck the halls. Each bird adds a "la" to the chorus. Caption: "Deck the halls with boughs of holly...Christmas 1981."

White Satin, 3¼″ diam.
450QX803-5, $4.50 ☐

Joan Walsh Anglund©

Front — three Anglund children are decorating the stair rail. Back — the three are seated on a green couch reading from a book. The couch is on a braided rug with a decorated tree at one side and a table with lighted candle at the other. Caption: " 'Tis the time of dreams come true. 'Tis the time for merrymaking" and "Christmas 1981."

White Satin, 3¼″ diam.
450QX804-2, $4.50 ☐

DISNEY

Sorcerer's apprentice Mickey Mouse creates the magic of a decorated, candlelit tree filled with presents and toys against deep blue of star-sprinkled nighttime sky. Caption: "Christmas 1981" and "Christmas is a time of magic, it's the season of surprise, everything begins to sparkle right before your very eyes."

White Satin, 3¼″ diam.
450QX805-5, $4.50 ☐

Christmas 1981 - Schneeberg, Christmas Magic, Traditional (Black Santa), Let Us Adore Him

Decorative Ball Ornaments

Christmas 1981 — Schneeberg

Design reproduced from a photograph of a Schneeberg collage has birds, beads, musical instruments, and candy on a white background. A Christmas tree decorated with birds, animals, beads, and candy is central motif. Santa is pictured leaving array of toys under it. Back — beautiful sunburst made of beads and colored glass ball ornaments is centered with dated banner. Caption: "1981."

White Satin, 3¼" diam.
450QX809-5, $4.50 ☐

Christmas Magic

A gnomelike Santa and animals are ice skating. Caption: "Christmas 1981" and "It's here, there, everywhere...Christmas magic's in the air."

White Satin, 3¼" diam.
450QX810-2, $4.50 ☐

Traditional (Black Santa)

Front — Santa feeds his animal friends in a snowy forest. Back — wreath-framed Santa gives a merry wave. Caption: "It's Christmas. It's time for sharing...and dreaming, and caring and merry gift bearing..." and "1981."

White Satin, 3¼" diam.
450QX801-5, $4.50 ☐

Let Us Adore Him

A beautiful, radiant scene of the Nativity with cherubim adoring the Christ Child in the manger. The background is dark brown. Caption: "Christmas 1981" and "O come let us adore him."

Gold Glass, 3¼" diam.
450QX811-5, $4.50 ☐

Santa's Coming

Front — Santa holds the reins of his toy-filled sleigh while Mrs. Santa makes sure his scarf is wrapped snugly around his neck. The reindeers are poised and ready. Back — Santa and his reindeers are flying through the air on a moonlit night. Caption: "Christmas 1981" and "Hustle, bustle, hurry, scurry, Santa's coming...never worry."

White Satin, 3¼" diam.
450QX812-2, $4.50 ☐

Christmas in the Forest

On a snowy Christmas night the animals and birds admire the white blossoms peeking through the snow. Caption: "Christmas 1981" and "Softly...gently...joyfully... Christmas arrives in the heart."

Gold Glass, 3¼" diam.
450QX813-5, $4.50 ☐

Santa's Coming, Christmas in the Forest, Merry Christmas, Santa's Surprise

Crown Classics: Angel, Tree Photoholder, Unicorn

Frosted Images: Angel, Mouse, Snowman

Merry Christmas

Front — gold-accented burgundy diamonds with tiny red flowers on green background centered with "1981." Back — same design with colors reversed. Caption: "Merry Christmas 1981."

Gold Glass, $3\frac{1}{4}$" diam.
450QX814-2, $4.50 ☐

Santa's Surprise

On a wintry night Santa plucks the stars from the deep blue sky and uses them to decorate a small evergreen tree in the snow. Caption: "Twinkle, glimmer, sparkle, shimmer. . .let the Christmas season shine" and "Christmas 1981."

White Satin, $3\frac{1}{4}$" diam.
450QX815-5, $4.50 ☐

Crown Classics

Angel

Golden-haired angel with white wings is wearing long robe in shades of red which is tied with a green sash. Designed with the look of leaded stained glass.

Acrylic, $3\frac{3}{4}$" tall
450QX507-5, $4.50 ☐

Tree Photoholder

Front — green Christmas tree decorated with multicolored ornaments has a round opening to hold a photograph. Back — design repeat and captions in gold. Caption: "Christmas 1981."

Acrylic, $3\frac{27}{32}$" tall
550QX515-5, $5.50 ☐

Unicorn

Front — graceful unicorn in white cameo is shown on a soft green background. Back — raised floral medallions frame white lettered caption. Caption: "A time of magical moments, dreams come true. . .Christmas 1981."

Light Green Cameo, $3\frac{3}{8}$" diam.
850QX516-5, $8.50 ☐

Frosted Images

Three frosted, three-dimensional ornaments with the look of etched crystal. Ranging in size from $1\frac{15}{32}$" to $1\frac{19}{32}$" tall, they were priced at $4.00

400QX508-2 Mouse ☐
400QX509-5 Angel ☐
400QX510-2 Snowman ☐

Holiday Highlights: Shepherd Scene, Christmas Star

Little Trimmers: Puppy Love, Jolly Snowman, Perky Penguin, Clothespin Drummer Boy, The Stocking Mouse

Holiday Highlights

Shepherd Scene

A shepherd with his sheep see the distant city of Bethlehem glowing by the light of the star. Caption is stamped with silver foil. Caption: "Christmas 1981."

Clear Acrylic, 4" tall
550QX500-2, $5.50 ☐

Christmas Star

Star with a raised, faceted border has emerald shapes tucked between the points. Silver foil stamping accents the caption. Caption: "Christmas 1981."

Clear Acrylic, 3½" tall
550QX501-5, $5.50 ☐

Little Trimmers

Puppy Love

A bread-dough look tan puppy with a red heart on his chest and a cord of real red ribbon around his neck.

Handcrafted, 1 5/32" tall
350QX406-2, $3.50 ☐

Jolly Snowman

Smiling snowman wears a black top hat and a real fabric scarf.

Handcrafted, 2 7/32" tall
350QX407-5, $3.50 ☐

Perky Penguin

Tiny penguin wears a red cap and red and green striped scarf.

Handcrafted, 1 5/16" tall
350QX409-5, $3.50 ☐

Clothespin Drummer Boy

Drummer boy dressed in a black and brown uniform and a red hat beats his red drum.

Handcrafted, 2 13/16" tall
450QX408-2, $4.50 ☐

The Stocking Mouse

A white mouse wearing a blue-and-white polka dot nightcap peeks out of the top of a green and red real knit stocking.

Handcrafted, 2¼" tall
450QX412-2, $4.50 ☐

Handcrafted Ornaments

Space Santa

Space-helmeted Santa is flying in a silver suit carrying a dated silver star. Caption: "1981."

Handcrafted, 3" tall
650QX430-2, $6.50 ☐

Candyville Express
A locomotive designed with the look of sugar-coated gumdrops has wheels of "cookies" and "licorice candy."

Handcrafted, 3" long
750QX418-2, $7.50 ☐

Ice Fairy
A lovely white ice fairy with frosted acrylic wings holds a clear acrylic snowflake.

Handcrafted & Acrylic, 4⅛" tall
650QX431-5, $6.50 ☐

Star Swing
Little girl dressed in red, blue, and green swings from a chrome-plated brass star with the date on it.

Brass & Handcrafted, 3⅝" tall
550QX421-5, $5.50 ☐

A Heavenly Nap
Design is reissued from 1980. (See 1980 Annual Collection.)

Handcrafted, 3¼" tall
650QX139-4, $6.50

Dough Angel
In the style of bread-dough, a little angel wearing a blue-and-white dress holds a star. A reissue from 1978. (See 1978 Annual Collection.)

Handcrafted, 2 15/16" tall
550QX139-6, $5.50

Topsy-Turvy Tunes
An opossum hangs by his tail from a tree branch, while a little red bird perches on the songbook that the opossum is holding. Caption: "Carols" on the green book cover.

Handcrafted, 3" tall
750QX429-5, $7.50 ☐

A Well-Stocked Stocking
Real knit red-and-white stocking is filled to capacity with a doll, jack-in-the-box, candy cane, and other toys.

Handcrafted, 4½" tall
900QX154-7, $9.00 ☐

The Friendly Fiddler
A rabbit wearing a green and red scarf plays a Christmas tune on a fiddle tucked under his chin.

Handcrafted, 3 5/32" tall
800QX434-2, $8.00 ☐

The Ice Sculptor
Bear "artist" in red smock and green tam is busily sculpting a self portrait in ice (clear acrylic).

Handcrafted, 3 1/32" tall
800QX432-2, $8.00 ☐

Space Santa, Candyville Express, Ice Fairy, Star Swing

Topsy-Turvy Tunes, A Well-Stocked Stocking, The Friendly Fiddler, The Ice Sculptor

Christmas Dreams

Front — this peek-through design shows a little boy dressed in a blue snowsuit, white scarf, and brown knit cap admiring a teddy bear displayed in a toy shop window. Back — peek-through view from inside the toy store. Caption: "Toy Shop 1981."

Handcrafted, 3¼" diam.
1200QX437-5, $12.00 ☐

Christmas Fantasy

A graceful white goose with a real brass ribbon caught in his bill gives a ride to an elf astride his back. The elf is dressed in red and green.

Handcrafted, 3¾" long
1300QX155-4, $13.00 ☐

Sailing Santa

Santa is sailing in the basket of a red hot air balloon. Green-and-red Christmas stockings are used for weights on the basket. The balloon has gold painted trim and white caption and date. Caption: "Merry Christmas 1981."

Handcrafted, 5" tall
1300QX439-5, $13.00 ☐

Love and Joy (Porcelain Chimes)

White bisque chimes are comprised of three white doves suspended from a white heart bearing impressed caption and date. Chimes have red fabric ribbon. Caption: "1981."

Porcelain, 3¾" tall
900QX425-2, $9.00 ☐

Drummer Boy

This hand-painted drummer boy is made of real wood and has movable arms and legs.

Wood, 3½" tall
250QX148-1, $2.50 ☐

St. Nicholas

Traditional European St. Nicholas wearing a long coat holds a lantern to light his way as he makes his rounds delivering presents from his pack.

Pressed Tin, 4⅜" tall
550QX446-2, $5.50 ☐

Mr. & Mrs. Claus

Mr. & Mrs. Claus are reissued from their introductory year, 1975. Santa has a kitten on his shoulder and Mrs. Claus, wearing a red dress, white bonnet and apron, holds two kittens in her arms. (See 1975 Annual Collection.)

Handcrafted, 3¾" tall
1200QX448-5, 2 in box $12.00

Christmas Dreams front and back

Christmas Fantasy, Sailing Santa

Love and Joy, Drummer Boy, St. Nicholas

Holiday Chimes: Snowman Chime

Checking It Twice
This popular Santa is a reissue from 1980. (See 1980 Annual Collection.)

Handcrafted, 5 15/16" tall
2250QX158-4, $22.50

New Collectible Series: Rocking Horse - First Edition

Holiday Chimes

Snowman Chimes

New in the chimes collection is the Snowman and his family. Mr. Snowman wears a top hat and holds a straw broom. Mrs. Snowman has a design on her dress, and the Snowchild wearing a knit-type hat holds a cane and gift. They are suspended from a large snowflake.

Chrome Plate, 4" tall
550QX445-5, $5.50 ☐

Santa Mobile

550QX136-1, Reissue from 1980, $5.50

Snowflake Chimes

550QX165-4, Reissue from 1980, $5.50

(See 1980 Annual Collection for photographs and descriptions of these reissues.)

Collectible Series

Rocking Horse — First Edition

A brown and white palomino horse with tail of real brown yarn is rocking along on dated red rockers. Saddle is red and the blanket under the saddle is blue. Caption: "1981."

Handcrafted, 2" tall
900QX422-2, $9.00 ☐

Collectible Series

Bellringer — Third Edition Swingin' Bellringer

The clapper of this gold-rimmed porcelain bell is a candy cane with a mouse wearing a green cap sitting in its curve. Third design in this series. Caption: "1981" in the center of fired-on wreath decal.

Ceramic & Handcrafted, 4" tall
1500QX441-5, $15.00 ☐

Norman Rockwell — Second Edition "Carolers"

Front — delicate white cameo representation of Rockwell's "Carolers." Back — caption in white letters. Caption: "Carolers, second in a series, the Norman Rockwell Collection Christmas 1981."

Dark Blue Cameo, 3 3/8" diam.
850QX511-5, $8.50 ☐

Here Comes Santa — Third Edition Rooftop Deliveries

Santa changed his mode of transportation this year. He "drives" over roofs in a vehicle that resembles an old milk truck. The roof of the truck is green. The sign on the side is ornately printed in red, deep yellow, and green. The black tired wheels have golden spokes. Third design in this series. Caption: "S. Claus & Co. Rooftop Deliveries 1981."

Handcrafted, 4 1/16" tall
1300QX438-2, $13.00 ☐

Carrousel — Fourth Edition Skaters Carrousel

Fourth design in this series features a family of four ice-skating around a green pole in the center of the carrousel. Carrousel top has hand-painted bands of green, red, and blue with white snowflakes. The date is stamped on the top edge of the carrousel roof. Caption: "1981."

Handcrafted, 2 15/32" tall
900QX427-5, $9.00 ☐

SNOOPY and Friends — Third Edition

A "birdsled" team of Woodstock and friends is pulling SNOOPY past a SNOOPY snowman. The snowman is wearing a black top hat and green scarf. A sign in the snow is dated. This is third design in this series. Caption: "1981."

Handcrafted, 3 1/4" diam.
1200QX436-2, $12.00 ☐

Collectible Series: The Bellringer - Third Edition; Norman Rockwell - Second Edition; Here Comes Santa - Third Edition; Carrousel - Fourth Edition

Collectible Series: Snoopy and Friends - Third Edition; Thimble - Fourth Edition; Frosty Friends - Second Edition

Sewn Ornaments: Peppermint Mouse, Gingham Dog, Calico Kitty, Cardinal Cutie

Plush Ornaments: Christmas Teddy, Raccoon Tunes

Thimble — Fourth Edition

A flying angel with white wings and brass halo is holding a diminutive Christmas tree that is potted in a thimble. Her pink robe is edged in gold.

Handcrafted, 1½" diam.
450QX413-5, $4.50 ☐

Frosty Friends — Second Edition

An Eskimo and a Husky puppy are sheltered snugly in an igloo. Date over the entrance is framed with green holly and red berries. This is the second design in this series. Caption: "1981."

Handcrafted, 2" tall
800QX433-5, $8.00 ☐

Yarn and Fabric Ornaments

Sewn Ornaments

New for 1981, these darling fabric animals feature ribbon trims and quilting details. All are 3" tall and priced at $3.00

300QX400-2 Cardinal Cutie ☐
300QX401-5 Peppermint Mouse ☐
300QX402-2 Gingham Dog ☐
300QX403-5 Calico Kitty ☐

Yarn Ornaments

The four designs in this series were reissued from 1980 by popular demand. (See 1980 Annual Collection for photograph and description.)

Plush Animals

Two charming plush animals were new introductions in 1981 and were individually packaged in gift boxes.

Christmas Teddy

Teddy wears a red knitted stocking cap and perky plaid ribbon bow.

Plush, 4" tall
550QX404-2, $5.50 ☐

Raccoon Tunes

Merry raccoon caroler is clad in felt vest and holds a felt songbook.

Plush, 4" tall
550QX405-5, $5.50 ☐

THE 1982 COLLECTION

In 1982 Hallmark's Keepsake Ornament Collection celebrated its tenth issue year by introducing three new series of collectible ornaments. Making their first appearances were the Holiday Wildlife series, the Tin Locomotive series, and the Clothespin series.

Six decorative glass ball ornaments were introduced in a special "Designer Keepsakes" offering which included a clear glass ball ornament featuring a permanent, fired-on decal. Four new ornament formats were added to the line: cloisonné, hand-embroidered fabric, sculptured acrylic, and dimensional brass ornaments.

The end of the first decade also marked the adoption of a new procedure specially created to assist Keepsake collectors. Beginning in 1982, all of the ornaments in the Collector's Series were stamped with an identifying Christmas Tree symbol or the words "—— in a series" (which permanently documents which issue the item is in the series). An edition number was also printed in the tree symbol to mark the ornament's issue date. The new identifying symbols made collecting easier and more exciting for the Hallmark Keepsake collectors — a group which represented 65 percent of all Hallmark Keepsake Ornament purchasers in 1982.

Commemoratives

Baby's First Christmas - Photoholder

Red-and-white Christmas stocking filled with toys, candy, and gifts. Caption appears on the back. Caption: "Baby's First Christmas 1982" and "Oh what joy and sweet surprise Christmas brings to little eyes."

Acrylic, 4¼" tall
650QX312-6, $6.50 ☐

Baby's First Christmas

A baby's white rattle with a peek-in window showing baby taking a nap in a crib beside a window. Gold handle topped with red ring is tied in green ribbon. All hand painted. Caption: "Baby's First Christmas 1982."

Handcrafted, 3" tall
1300QX455-3, $13.00 ☐

Baby's First Christmas (Boy)

Most uniquely, this design was actually hand embroidered by an artist and then photographed for this ornament. The baby girl ornament was also created in the same manner. Caption: "Baby's First Christmas 1982" and "A baby boy is a precious gift — a blessing from above."

Light Blue Satin, 3¼" diam.
450QX216-3, $4.50 ☐

Baby's First Christmas (Girl)

Embroidered toys for a baby girl form a quilt motif. Caption: "Baby's First Christmas 1982" and "A baby girl is the sweetest gift a lifetime can provide."

Light Pink Satin, 3¼" diam.
450QX207-3, $4.50 ☐

Baby's First Christmas - Photoholder, Handcrafted, For Boy, For Girl

Godchild

A little angel stands on a holly bough to reach an elusive snowflake. Caption: "Merry Christmas to a Special Godchild. 1982."

White Glass, 3¼" diam.
450QX222-6, $4.50 ☐

Grandson

Bunnies sledding in the snow. Caption: "A Grandson...makes days bright, hearts light and Christmas time a real delight. Christmas 1982."

White Satin, 3¼" diam.
450QX224-6, $4.50 ☐

Granddaughter

Puppies, teddy bears, and bunnies hold a rope of green garland which encircles the ornament. This design was reproduced from a three-dimensional soft sculpture. Caption: "A Granddaughter has a special gift for giving special joy" and "Christmas 1982."

White Satin, 3¼" diam.
450QX224-3, $4.50 ☐

Son

Marching band dressed in red and teal blue uniforms keeps perfect step on a caramel-colored background. Caption: "A Son is the pride of your heart, the joy of your life" and "Christmas 1982."

Caramel Soft-Sheen Satin, 3¼" diam.
450QX204-3, $4.50 ☐

Daughter

Colors of peppermint pink, candy cane red, and soft pastels are used to illustrate tempting array of Christmas goodies. Caption: "A Daughter's love makes Christmas special. 1982."

Ecru Soft-Sheen Satin, 3¼" diam.
450QX204-6, $4.50 ☐

Father

Framed, hand colored, woodcut-style artwork bands this ornament. Caption: "A Father's love brightens the season" and "Christmas 1982."

Ecru Soft-Sheen Satin, 3¼" diam.
450QX205-6, $4.50 ☐

Mother

Front — poinsettia bouquet tied in pink ribbons. Back — holly and pine garland around caption. Caption: "The spirit of Christmas lives in a Mother's loving heart. Christmas 1982."

White Glass, 3¼" diam.
450QX205-3, $4.50 ☐

Godchild, Grandson, Granddaughter, Son, Daughter

Father, Mother, Mother and Dad, Sister

Mother and Dad

Sprays of holly leaves, berries, and evergreens caught with red ribbons form beautiful contrast against the white porcelain glass. Caption: "A Mother and Dad know so many ways to warm a heart with love" and "Christmas 1982."

White Porcelain Glass, 3¼" diam.
450QX222-3, $4.50 ☐

Sister

Front — small girl ice skating on a pond with three houses in the background. Back — the girl petting a white bunny. All in soft pastels. This is a new introduction of an ornament commemorating Sister. Caption: "A Sister brings the beauty of memories and the warmth of love to Christmas 1982."

White Glass, 3¼" diam.
450QX208-3, $4.50 ☐

Grandmother, Grandfather, Grandparents

First Christmas Together: Cameo, Glass Ball, Brass Locket

Grandmother

Patchwork quilt effect of lace, ribbon, fabric, and embroidery. Caption: "A Grandmother is love. Christmas 1982."

Dark Pink Satin, 3¼" diam.
450QX200-3, $4.50 ☐

Grandfather

A graceful deer amid feathery scrolls. Caption: "Grandfather...in his strength he teaches, in his gentleness he loves. Christmas 1982."

Dark Blue Satin, 3¼" diam.
450QX207-6, $4.50 ☐

Grandparents

Homes on snow covered hillsides, an ice skating outing, and an old covered bridge. Caption: "With thoughts of Grandparents come thoughts of days the heart will always treasure" and "Christmas 1982."

White Glass, 3¼" diam.
450QX214-6, $4.50 ☐

First Christmas Together

Dressed in style of Charles Dickens' characters, a couple ice skate together. Caption: "Christmas is for sharing with the special one you love." and "First Christmas Together 1982."

Turquoise Cameo, 3⅜" diam.
850QX306-6, $8.50 ☐

First Christmas Together

Delicate frosty background gives lacy, silvered effect to stark bare trees. A pair of redbirds soaring in the snowy mist symbolize the caption. Caption: "Quiet moments together...love that lasts forever" and "First Christmas Together 1982."

Silver Chrome Glass, 3¼" diam.
450QX211-3, $4.50 ☐

First Christmas Together — Locket

Dimensional, hinged, heart-shaped brass locket opens to become two hearts, each with insert for a photo. Includes brass hanger. Caption: "First Christmas Together 1982."

Polished Brass, 2⅝" tall
1500QX456-3, $15.00 ☐

Christmas Memories

Square white frame is trimmed in red ribbon and green holly leaves. Outline of red bow shapes the top which has tab for hanging on the tree. The caption is stamped in raised letters on the back of the design. Caption: "How bright the joys of Christmas, how warm the memories" and "1982."

Acrylic, 4⅛" tall
650QX311-6, $6.50 ☐

Teacher

Elves in their antics cast shadows that spell "CHRISTMAS 1982." The last elf holds up an apple with the caption on the gift tag. Caption: "To a Special Teacher" and "Christmas 1982."

White Glass, 3¼" diam.
450QX214-3, $4.50 ☐

New Home

Nighttime scene of colorful village homes and snow-covered hillsides. Caption: "Christmas time fills hearts with love and homes with warmth and joy. 1982."

Dark Blue Satin, 3 1/4" diam.
450QX212-6, $4.50 ☐

Teacher

Snow-covered red schoolhouse has a belltower and Christmas tree at the side. Caption: "Merry Christmas to my Teacher" and "1982."

Acrylic, 3 15/16" tall
650QX312-3, $6.50 ☐

25th Christmas Together

Pictures the warm, welcoming glow of lighted windows on a frosty, snow-covered night. Caption: "Christmas...as timeless as snowfall, as forever as candleglow, as always as love" and "Twenty-fifth Christmas together 1982."

White Porcelain Glass, 3 1/4" diam.
450QX211-6, $4.50 ☐

50th Christmas Together

Gold-on-gold background has design of scrolled borders and ornate lettering in burgundy highlighted with white. Caption: "We measure our time, not by years alone, but by the love and joy we've known" and "50th Christmas Together 1982."

Gold Glass, 3 1/4" diam.
450QX212-3, $4.50 ☐

Moments of Love

Stagecoach with galloping team is silhouetted in white against deep blue sky sprinkled with snowflakes. Caption: "Each moment of love lives forever in memory" and "Christmas 1982."

Blue Soft-Sheen Satin, 3 1/4" diam.
450QX209-3, $4.50 ☐

Love

Wreaths of Christmas flowers and greenery frame the caption and date. Caption: "Christmas...season bright with love" and "Christmas 1982."

Ecru Soft-Sheen Satin, 3 1/4" diam.
450QX209-6, $4.50 ☐

Friendship

Happy animals ice skating merrily. Caption: "Hearts are happy when friends are together" and "Christmas 1982."

White Satin, 3 1/4" diam.
450QX208-6, $4.50 ☐

Christmas Memories Photoholder, Teacher: Glass Ball, New Home, Teacher Photoholder

Twenty-Fifth Christmas Together, Fiftieth Christmas Together, Moments of Love, Love, Friendship

Teacher, Baby's 1st Christmas, First Christmas Together, Love, Friendship

Teacher — Apple
A clear acrylic apple with green foil stamped leaves, red foil-stamped caption, and etched scrolls. Caption: "To a Special Teacher. 1982."

Acrylic, 3½" tall
550QX301-6, $5.50 ☐

Baby's First Christmas
Cuddly teddy bear in frosted acrylic holds clear acrylic block that contains caption which is stamped in silver foil. Caption: "Baby's First Christmas 1982."

Acrylic, 3¹⁷⁄₃₂" tall
550QX302-3, $5.50 ☐

First Christmas Together
A contemporary, tailored tree with caption and date stamped in silver foil. Caption: "1982" and "First Christmas Together."

Acrylic, 4¼" tall
550QX302-6, $5.50 ☐

Love
Heart-shaped with etched leaves and scrolls, and caption stamped in gold foil. Caption: "Love is forever between two hearts that share it. 1982."

Acrylic, 4⅛" tall
550QX304-3, $5.50 ☐

Friendship
Kitten in a stocking is held by a puppy wearing knitted Santa cap. Caption is stamped with silver foil. Caption: "Christmas is for friends 1982."

Acrylic, 3¼" tall
550QX304-6, $5.50 ☐

Property Ornaments

MISS PIGGY and KERMIT™
Front — MISS PIGGY™ lounges among gifts with a beautiful tree in the background. Back — KERMIT™ hangs Christmas balls on a garland. Caption: "Have yourself a lavish little Christmas" and "Season's greenings 1982."

White Satin, 3¼" diam.
450QX218-3, $4.50 ☐

MUPPETS™ Party
The whole MUPPETS™ gang is gathered for a Christmas party. There are musicians, carolers, gifts, and MISS PIGGY™ in her finery seated on the piano next to a tall candelabra. Caption: "Merry Christmas 1982."

White Satin, 3¼" diam.
450QX218-6, $4.50 ☐

KERMIT the FROG™
KERMIT™ is a real sport skiing down the slopes of the Christmas tree wearing red cap trimmed in white and red skiis and poles.

Handcrafted, 3³⁄₁₆" tall
1100QX495-6, $11.00 ☐

THE DIVINE MISS PIGGY™
Reissue from 1981. (See 1981 Annual Collection.)

Handcrafted, 4" long
1200QX425-5, $12.00

Betsey Clark
Little angel is decorating a Christmas tree while floating on a cloud. Caption: " 'Tis the season for trimming trees and making merry memories" and "Christmas 1982."

Blue Cameo, 3⅜" diam.
850QX305-6, $8.50 ☐

MISS PIGGY and KERMIT™, MUPPET™ Party, KERMIT the FROG™

Betsey Clark Cameo, Norman Rockwell - Third Edition, Betsey Clark - 10th Edition, Norman Rockwell Satin Ball

PEANUTS®, DISNEY, Mary Hamilton, Joan Walsh Anglund©

Norman Rockwell — Third Edition

Design in white on red of Christmas mantel and Santa laughing at a very tiny stocking he is supposed to fill. Caption and date stamped in silver foil are on the back. Caption: "Filling the Stockings. Third in a Series. The Norman Rockwell Collection. Christmas 1982."

Red Cameo, 3⅜" diam.
850QX305-3, $8.50 ☐

Betsey Clark — Tenth Edition

Three children in their nighties share a bedtime story beside a tiny decorated Christmas tree and wrapped gifts. Caption: "The joys of Christmas are multiplied when shared with those we love" and "Christmas 1982."

White Satin, 3¼" diam.
450QX215-6, $4.50 ☐

Norman Rockwell

A young boy pictured in three panels is putting on a Santa suit and stuffing a pillow in the front of the pants; carolling enthusiastically in church; and dressed in robe and pajamas holding a candle. Caption: "From the Norman Rockwell Collection 1982. Hearts are light, smiles are bright, child's delight, it's Christmas."

Red Soft-Sheen Satin, 3¼" diam.
450QX202-3, $4.50 ☐

PEANUTS®

SNOOPY cycles his way into the holidays riding a tandem bicycle with Woodstock and the flock. Caption: "Christmas 1982."

Light Blue Satin, 3¼" diam.
450QX200-6, $4.50 ☐

DISNEY

The Seven Dwarfs are carrying candy canes, toys, gifts, wreath, and the tree as they prepare for Christmas. Caption: "Christmas...time for surprises — in all shapes and sizes" and "1982."

White Satin, 3½" diam.
450QX217-3, $4.50 ☐

Mary Hamilton

Tiny angels are ringing bells, floating on clouds, and perched on musical notes as they sing and play Christmas carols. Caption: "Joy to the world. 1982."

Blue Soft-Sheen Satin, 3¼" diam.
450QX217-6, $4.50 ☐

Joan Walsh Anglund©

Joan Walsh Anglund's children admire a snow-laden tree with a gold star on top. Caption: "Friends make Christmas memories. 1982."

White Satin, 3¼" diam.
450QX219-3, $4.50 ☐

Designer Keepsakes: Old World Angels, Patterns of Christmas, Old Fashioned Christmas

Designer Keepsakes: Stained Glass, Merry Christmas, Twelve Day of Christmas

Designer Keepsakes

Old World Angels

Old-world angels holding lighted candles float amid stars and streamers.

White Porcelain Glass, 3¼" diam.
450QX226-3, $4.50 ☐

Patterns of Christmas

Oriental designs of poinsettias and holly are highlighted in gold. The use of gold inks adds extra richness to this elegant design.

Gold Glass, 3¼" diam.
450QX226-6, $4.50 ☐

Old Fashioned Christmas

Reproduction of antique English greeting cards from the late 1800s depicts children decorating for Christmas. Caption "Merry Christmas" and "Happy New Year."

White Porcelain Glass, 3¼" diam.
450QX227-6, $4.50 ☐

Stained Glass

Created in the style of a leaded, stained glass window, design of holly and poinsettias forms pleasing contrast with panels of lavender, blue, and green. The use of pearlized inks makes this design shimmer.

White Glass, 3¼" diam.
450QX228-3, $4.50 ☐

Merry Christmas

This design is the first to use fired-on decal application to a clear glass ball. Caption: "Merry Christmas" and "Happy Holidays."

Clear Glass, 3¼" diam.
450QX225-6, $4.50 ☐

Twelve Days of Christmas

Attractive painting illustrates the verses of favorite old Christmas carol. White pebbled glass captures the look of a snowscape realistically. Caption: "The Twelve Days of Christmas 1982."

White Pebbled Glass, 3¼" diam.
450QX203-6, $4.50 ☐

Decorative Ball Ornaments

Christmas Angel

Beautiful angel on a deep blue background shelters the flame of a glowing candle. Caption: "From Heaven above the light of love shines into our hearts at Christmas" and "1982."

Gold Glass, 3¼" diam.
450QX220-6, $4.50 ☐

Christmas Angel, Santa, Currier and Ives, A Season for Caring

Colors of Christmas: Nativity, Santa's Flight

Ice Sculptures: Snowy Seal, Artic Penguin

Santa

Front — a close-up of Santa. Back — Santa smoking his pipe. Caption: "His eyes, how they twinkled, his dimples, how merry" and "Christmas 1982."

White Porcelain Glass, 3¼" diam.
450QX221-6, $4.50 ☐

Currier & Ives

This reproduction of "The Road — Winter" is from an original Currier and Ives print "registered according to an Act of Congress in 1853." A couple takes an afternoon sleigh ride on a country road. Caption: "Christmas 1982" and "The Road — Winter"; "Currier and Ives."

White Porcelain Glass, 3¼" diam.
450QX201-3, $4.50 ☐

Season for Caring

A beautiful soft blue night scene of the star shining over Bethlehem. A little shepherd with his sheep are following the star. Caption: "Christmas...Season for caring" and "1982."

Light Blue Soft-Sheen Satin, 3¼" diam.
450QX221-3, $4.50 ☐

Colors of Christmas

Nativity

Traditional portrayal of the Holy Family is shown in the look of a leaded, stained glass window.

Acrylic, 4" tall
450QX308-3, $4.50 ☐

Santa's Flight

Santa aboard a hot air balloon is created in stained glass style. Caption "Christmas 1982."

Acrylic, 4¼" tall
450QX308-6, $4.50 ☐

Ice Sculptures

Snowy Seal

A happy, smiling seal is sculptured in clear acrylic.

Clear Acrylic, 1 19/32" tall
400QX300-6, $4.00 ☐

Arctic Penguin

A penguin molded in clear acrylic.

Clear Acrylic, 1½" tall
400QX300-3, $4.00 ☐

Holiday Highlights

Christmas Sleigh

A sleigh bearing gifts and a Christmas tree has runners and caption that are stamped in silver foil. Caption: "Christmas 1982."

Acrylic, $3\frac{23}{32}$" tall
550QX309-3, $5.50 ☐

Angel

Angel wearing flowing gown plays a heavenly harp. Caption is stamped in gold foil. Caption: "Rejoice."

Acrylic, $3\frac{1}{2}$" tall
550QX309-6, $5.50 ☐

Christmas Magic

Etched design is of a little rabbit admiring an ornament hanging from a bough. This Crown Classic is in the shape of an oval Christmas ornament with scrolling that outlines the cap at the top. The caption is stamped with silver foil. Caption: "Christmas. . .season of magical moments."

Acrylic, $3\frac{13}{16}$" tall
550QX311-3, $5.50 ☐

Handcrafted Ornaments

Three Kings

On a dark blue background the Three Kings are traveling to the city of Bethlehem shown in the distance. Caption: "By a star shining brightly, Three Kings set their course and followed the heavenly light to its source" and "1982."

Blue Cameo, $3\frac{3}{8}$" diam.
850QX307-3, $8.50 ☐

Baroque Angel

A beautiful cherubim wearing a regal lavender ribbon is holding a pole with a stamped brass banner as he flies into Christmas. Caption: "Joyeux Noel."

Brass and Handcrafted, $4\frac{7}{16}$" tall
1500QX456-6, $15.00 ☐

Cloisonné Angel

An open heart with blue enameled leaf border is centered with an angel herald enameled in blue, white, and red. On the reverse of the angel are the words "Peace, Love, Joy" in raised letters.

Cloisonné, $2\frac{21}{32}$" tall
1200QX145-4, $12.00 ☐

Holiday Highlights: Christmas Sleigh, Angel, Christmas Magic

Three Kings, Baroque Angel, Cloisonne Angel

Brass Ornaments: Santa and Reindeer, Brass Bell, Santa's Sleigh

Brass Ornaments

Unique ornaments crafted of highly polished brass are lacquer-coated to prevent tarnishing. These distinctive ornaments were introduced in 1982.

Santa and Reindeer

Santa flies through the night in a brass runnered sleigh drawn by four stamped-brass reindeer.

Brass and Handcrafted, 2 9/32" tall
900QX467-6, $9.00 ☐

Brass Bell

Stamped design of holly leaves and berries decorates top and rim of handsomely paneled bell. Topped with red bow and ribbon for hanging.

Polished Brass, 2 11/32" tall
1200QX460-6, $12.00 ☐

Santa's Sleigh

Stamped design of Santa in a sleigh filled with toys.

Polished Brass, 2 5/8" tall
900QX478-6, $9.00 ☐

Handcrafted Ornaments

The Spirit of Christmas

Santa flies around the tree waving at onlookers in a silver colored, red trimmed, old-fashioned biplane. Caption: "The Spirit of Christmas 1982."

Handcrafted, 1 29/32" tall
1000QX452-6, $10.00 ☐

Jogging Santa

A sporty Santa in red-and-white jogging suit, green jogging shoes, and a brass jingle bell on the end of his cap is practicing for the great "All Christmas Marathon." His sweater is dated "82."

Handcrafted, 2 27/32" tall
800QX457-6, $8.00 ☐

Santa Bell

Realistic Santa dressed in red and white wears black boots which ring the bell.

Hand-decorated Porcelain, 3 11/16" tall
1500QX148-7, $15.00 ☐

Spirit of Christmas, Jogging Santa, Santa Bell, Santa's Workshop, Cycling Santa

Santa's Workshop

Santa is busy painting a dollhouse in his snow-covered cottage that is all decorated for Christmas. Cottage is open so one can peek in from three sides.

Handcrafted, 3" tall
1000QX450-3, $10.00 ☐

Cycling Santa

Santa pedals an old "velocipede" with wheels that actually turn. The handlebar basket holds a special present, and his toy-filled pack is safely stowed behind. Three brass bells attached to his pack jingle merrily.

Handcrafted, 4 3/8" tall
2000QX435-5, $20.00 ☐

Cowboy Snowman, Pinecone Home, Raccoon Surprises, Elfin Artist

Christmas Fantasy
Reissue from 1981. (See 1981 Annual Collection.)
Brass and Handcrafted, 3¾" long
1300QX155-4, $13.00

Cowboy Snowman
Dressed in the latest Western fashion, snowman is ready for the "Christmas Rodeo." He is wearing a red cowboy hat with a green band, red handkerchief around his neck, rope on his shoulder, green gloves, a cowboy belt, and red cowboy boots. He holds a candy cane. Mr. Snowman, rodeo time is a bit warm for you!
Handcrafted, 2 27/32" tall
800QX480-6, $8.00 ☐

Pinecone Home
Little white mouse in red pajamas and nightcap peeks out of the shuttered window of his cozy pinecone home and sees his filled stocking. A red fabric ribbon bow adorns the top.
Handcrafted, 2 23/32" tall
800QX461-3, $8.00 ☐

Raccoon Surprises
A roguish little raccoon is standing on a tree branch while raiding a red, green, and white argyle Christmas stocking. His redbird friend watches from his shoulder.
Handcrafted, 3" tall
900QX479-3, $9.00 ☐

Elfin Artist
Little bearded elf hangs onto his bucket of red paint as he swings from a bosun's chair while painting the stripes on a piece of ribbon candy.
Handcrafted, 3" tall
900QX457-3, $9.00 ☐

Ice Sculptor
Reissue from 1981. (See 1981 Annual Collection.)
Handcrafted, 3 1/32" tall
800QX432-2, $8.00

Tin Soldier
A proper British soldier stands at stiff attention, holding a rifle in his right hand and saluting left-handed. Uniform is gray, red, and white. Tall hat is black.
Pressed Tin, 4⅞" tall
650QX483-6, $6.50 ☐

Peeking Elf
Little elf peeks over the top of a silver ball ornament which is diagonally tied in red ribbon.
Handcrafted, 3 3/32" tall
650QX419-5, $6.50 ☐

Jolly Christmas Tree
A smiling Christmas tree, dressed in Christmas finery and a gumdrop "topper," waves a star as he "flies" into Christmas.
Handcrafted, 2 13/16" tall
650QX465-3, $6.50 ☐

Embroidered Tree
Dark green fabric tree is decorated with hand-embroidered red, yellow, blue, orange, and pink flowers. The base and tree are trimmed in red braided cord.
Fabric, 4 9/16" tall
650QX494-6, $6.50 ☐

Little Trimmers

Cookie Mouse
A star-shaped cookie, outlined in green icing with a dated center in red, has lost one of its points to the cute little white mouse who sits on top happily munching the tasty morsel. Caption: "1982."
Handcrafted, 2 1/16" tall
450QX454-6, $4.50 ☐

Musical Angel
Tiny angel with a brass halo and dressed in blue plays a lyre while floating on a cloud.
Handcrafted, 1 15/16" tall
550QX459-6, $5.50 ☐

Merry Moose
Lovable young moose, caught up in his middle with red leather strappings, has lost his balance while ice skating.
Handcrafted, 1¾" tall
550QX415-5, $5.50 ☐

Christmas Owl
Reissue from 1980. (See 1980 Annual Collection)
Handcrafted, 1⅞" tall
450QX131-4, $4.50

Dove Love
A white dove swings in the center of a clear red heart in contemporary style.
Acrylic, 2 1/16" tall
450QX462-3, $4.50 ☐

Perky Penguin
Reissue from 1981. (See 1981 Annual Collection.)
Handcrafted, 1 5/16" tall
400QX409-5, $4.00

Christmas Kitten
Brown and white kitten wears a red fabric ribbon collar with brass bell attached.
Handcrafted, 1¼" tall
400QX454-3, $4.00 ☐

Jingling Teddy
Brown flocked teddy bear wearing a red fabric ribbon collar holds a brass bell.
Flocked, Brass, 2⅛" tall
400QX477-6, $4.00 ☐

Tin Soldier, Peeking Elf, Jolly Christmas Tree, Embroidered Tree

Cookie Mouse, Musical Angel, Merry Moose

Dove Love, Christmas Kitten, Jiggling Teddy

Collectible Series

Holiday Wildlife — First Edition

Round wooden plaque with white decoform inset (looks like porcelain). Inset has two red cardinals on a pine tree bough. First in a Collectible Series. Caption: "Cardinalis, Cardinalis. First in a series, Wildlife Collection Christmas 1982."

Wood and Decoform, 4" diam.
700QX313-3, $7.00 ☐

Tin Locomotive — First Edition

The first in the Tin Locomotive Series is reminiscent of the "Iron Horse" of early railroad days. Decorated in muted red, blue, and silver, it has a brass bell which hangs in front of the engineer's cab. Caption: "1982."

Pressed Tin, 3⅝" tall
1300QX460-3, $13.00 ☐

Clothespin Soldier — First Edition

In a red, white, and blue uniform and wearing a tall black hat, mustachioed clothespin soldier holds a black baton as if he were leading the future soldiers of this series who will fall in line behind him year by year.

Handcrafted, 3 5/32" tall
500QX458-3, $5.00 ☐

The Bellringer — Fourth Edition

The clapper is a handcrafted red-and-green wreath with a playful angel in its center. Caption: "1982" on a red banner trimmed in gold enclosing sprays of holly.

Ceramic & Handcrafted, 2 27/32" tall
1500QX455-6, $15.00 ☐

Carrousel Series — Fifth Edition

Snowmen holding hockey stock, broom, etc., are skating around in holiday frolic, wearing caps and a top hat. Caption: "Merry Christmas 1982" on the snow-covered top.

Handcrafted, 3" tall
1000QX478-3, $10.00 ☐

SNOOPY and Friends — Fourth Edition

SNOOPY plays Santa on Christmas Eve. He is seen leaving a snow-covered rooftop in a sleigh pulled by Woodstock and friends. Caption: "1982" on the red brick chimney.

Handcrafted, 3¼" diam.
1300QX480-3, $13.00 ☐

Collectible Series First Editions: Holiday Wildlife, Tin Locomotive, Clothespin Soldier

Collectible Series: The Bellringer-Fourth Edition; Carrousel-Fifth Edition; Snoopy and Friends-Fourth Edition; Here Comes Santa-Fourth Edition

Collectible Series: Rocking Horse-Second Edition; Thimble-Fifth Edition; Frosty Friends-Third Edition

Holiday Chimes: Bell Chime, Tree Chime

Here Comes Santa — Fourth Edition Jolly Trolley

Santa wearing conductor's cap is seated in the driver's seat of this lovely old trolley car. The colors are red, green, and tan. The rolled-up awnings are green and tan. Santa has a passenger. Caption: "1982 Jolly Trolley" in gold banner across the front.

Handcrafted, 3⅜″ tall
1500QX464-3, $15.00 ☐

Rocking Horse — Second Edition

This year's rocking horse is in the same style and size as the first rocking horse issued in 1981, except for color. The second issue is a black stallion with a tail of black yarn, a maroon saddle with blue blanket, and a maroon rocker bordered in gold.

Handcrafted, 2″ tall
1000QX502-3, $10.00 ☐

Thimble — Fifth Edition

Cute little white mouse "soldier" with big ears is standing at attention. He is wearing a red jacket, blue shirt, green necktie, and a silver colored thimble for a hat.

Handcrafted, 2 11/32″ tall
500QX451-3, $5.00 ☐

Frosty Friends — Third Edition

The little Eskimo scales an icicle "mountain." His little Husky friend sits at the top next to the dated flag.

Handcrafted, 4⅛″ tall
800QX452-3, $8.00 ☐

Holiday Chimes

Tree Chimes

Lacy, stamped brass tree has five bells and two doves incorporated into its leaf-filled branches.

Stamped Brass, 4 7/16″ tall
550QX484-6, $5.50 ☐

Bell Chimes

Three stamped bells, each with a different snowflake cutout, hang from a large snowflake.

Chrome-Plated Brass, 3″ tall
550QX494-3, $5.50 ☐

THE 1983 COLLECTION

The Hallmark Keepsake Ornament Collection entered its second decade with a tremendous new look. Commemorative ornaments were introduced in a new ceramic bell format, while Hallmark continued to expand its use of colors on ball ornaments. A variety of new shapes were introduced to supplement the traditional ball-shaped ornaments.

Porcelain ornaments were offered in several original designs, including a new Collectible Series which featured a porcelain teddy bear.

Satin ball ornaments received distinctive new caps in 1983 making them instantly recognizable by their Hallmark "crowns." New commemorative titles included Grandchild's First Christmas, Baby's Second Christmas, Child's Third Christmas, and Tenth Christmas Together.

Two Collectible Series ended in 1983 — the Carrousel ornaments (total of six editions) and the SNOOPY and Friends Panoramic Ball ornaments (total of five issues).

Commemoratives

Baby's First Christmas

In the new oval shape, an old-fashioned rocking horse is modeled in ivory on a red background. Caption is accented with silver foil stamping. Caption: "Baby's First Christmas 1983" and "A Baby fills each day with joy by filling hearts with love."

Red Cameo, 3¾" wide
750QX301-9, $7.50 ☐

Baby's First Christmas

Baby is in a cradle painted in a Folk Art-style Christmas motif. The fabric blanket and pillow are trimmed in lace and accented with a real ribbon bow. Cradle is captioned "Baby's First Christmas" and "1983."

Handcrafted, 3 5/32" tall
1400QX402-7, $14.00 ☐

Baby's First Christmas — Girl

Design is a reproduction of original stitchery of a red dress with white polka dots, a white apron pinafore, and a matching red bonnet. The pinafore pockets are filled with candy canes. The background is white bordered in green ribbon with flowers, ABC blocks, baby's rattle, and diaper pins. Caption: "A Baby Girl is a special gift of love." and "Baby's First Christmas 1983."

White Soft Sheen Satin, 3¼" diam.
450QX200-7, $4.50 ☐

Baby's First Christmas: Cameo, Handcrafted, Girl, Boy, Photoholder

Baby's First Christmas — Boy

Design features six tumbling teddy bears wearing blue sweaters and red scarfs. Caption: "A baby boy is love and joy...and pride that lasts a lifetime" and "Baby's First Christmas 1983."

Light Blue Soft Sheen Satin, 3 1/4" diam.
450QX200-9, $4.50

☐

Baby's First Christmas

An open baby book with area for inserting photograph. Caption: "A Baby is a dream fulfilled, a treasure to hold dear — a Baby is a love that grows more precious every year. Baby's First Christmas 1983."

Acrylic, 3 7/8" tall
700QX302-9, $7.00

☐

Grandchild's First Christmas

This is the first offering of this commemorative in any form. Baby rides in a white, wicker-look buggy with red wheels and green trim. Red, real cloth blanket with white dots carries caption. Caption: "Grandchild's First Christmas 1983."

Handcrafted, 3 3/4" long
1400QX430-9, $14.00

☐

Child's Third Christmas

Front — Santa with "1983." Back — "To Celebrate a Child's Third Christmas. How merry the season, how happy the day When Santa brings Christmas surprises your way." The ball is double wrapped in matt-textured and glossy satin to create a piqué effect — a new texture complimenting a new commemorative in the line.

White Satin Piqué, 3 1/4" diam.
450QX226-9, $4.50

☐

Grandchild's First Christmas

This commemorative ornament was specifically designed to fit the Classic shape introduced in 1983. Front — a baby with "A Grandchild is a special reason why Christmas is such a merry season." Back — toys and "Grandchild's First Christmas 1983."

Classic Shape, 3 1/4" diam.
600QX312-9, $6.00

☐

Baby's Second Christmas

Front — snowman, tree, and caption, "Baby's Second Christmas 1983." Back — snowpeople and caption, "A child knows such special ways to jolly up the holidays!"

White Soft Sheen Satin, 3 1/4" diam.
450QX226-7, $4.50

☐

Grandchild's First Christmas Handcrafted, Child's Third Christmas, Grandchild's First Christmas Classic Shape, Baby's Second Christmas

Granddaughter, Grandson, Son, Daughter, Godchild

Granddaughter

Three vignettes of artwork from the Hallmark Historical Collection, each picturing a young girl. A fourth vignette carries the caption and date. Caption: "A Granddaughter brings beautiful moments and memories to treasure" and "Christmas 1983."

White Porcelain Glass, 3¼" diam.
450QX202-7, $4.50 ☐

Grandson

A kitten plays with a red ornament as a puppy looks on. Caption: "Christmas 1983" and "A Grandson, like Christmas, brings joy to the heart."

Ecru Soft Sheen Satin, 3¼" diam.
450QX201-9, $4.50 ☐

Son

Little boy, house, Christmas trees, and snowman riding a snowhorse are depicted. Caption: "A Son brings a bit of Christmas cheer to every day throughout the year" and "1983."

Deep Blue Satin, 3¼" diam.
450QX202-9, $4.50 ☐

Daughter

In a reproduction based on original stitchery, rows of ruffled lace and velvet, and green and deep red ribbons are intermingled with pearls. The caption is on a card which is circled with pink flowers. Caption: "A Daughter's love makes Christmas beautiful 1983."

Pink Glass, 3¼" diam.
450QX203-7, $4.50 ☐

Godchild

Design features an angel and a tiny bird singing a holiday duet. Caption: "To wish a special Godchild a very merry Christmas 1983."

White Classical Glass, 3¼" diam.
450QX201-7, $4.50 ☐

Grandmother

A snowscene of a fenced-in farmhouse and barn shows a family approaching in a horse drawn sleigh. Caption: "Over the river and through the woods to Grandmother's house we go…Christmas 1983."

White Porcelain Glass, 3¼" diam.
450QX205-7, $4.50 ☐

Grandmother, Mother and Dad, Sister, Grandparents

Mom and Dad

White ceramic bell with a red fabric ribbon has fired-on decals of poinsettias and holly framing the captions. Caption: "Mom and Dad" and "Christmas 1983."

Ceramic, 3" tall
650QX429-7, $6.50 ☐

Sister

Candies, cookies, nuts, and a gingerbread man are pictured with flowers, ribbons, bows, basket, jars, and a wreath. Caption: "A Sister is a forever friend" and "1983."

White Classical Glass, 3¼" diam.
450QX206-9, $4.50 ☐

Grandparents

White ceramic bell with red fabric ribbon has fired on decals. Wreath on the front encircles "Christmas 1983." Caption on back: "Grandparents are love."

Ceramic, 3" tall
650QX429-9, $6.50 ☐

First Christmas Together

Candy canes form three hearts which surround the caption and the date. The design is printed directly on the surface of the ball. This is a new process for Hallmark. Caption: "First Christmas Together" and "1983."

White Glass, 3¼" diam.
450QX208-9, $4.50 ☐

First Christmas Together

A winter forest scene is shown in the newly introduced Classic shape. Caption: "First Christmas Together 1983" and "All the world is beautiful when seen through eyes of love."

Classic Shape, 3¼" diam.
600QX310-7, $6.00 ☐

First Christmas Together

In a new oval shape, an ivory relief of a couple in a horse-drawn sleigh is set against deep blue background. Caption is accented with silver foil stamping. Caption: "First Christmas Together 1983" and "Love is beauty shared, dreams come true…special memories made by two."

Dark Blue Cameo, 3¾" wide
750QX301-7, $7.50 ☐

First Christmas Together — Brass Locket

This polished brass locket opens to reveal space for two photos. Caption: "First Christmas Together 1983."

Polished Brass, 2⅝" tall
1500QX432-9, $15.00 ☐

First Christmas Together: Ball, Classic Shape, Cameo, Brass Heart.

Love is A Song, Love Handcrafted, Love Classic Shape, Love Glass Ball

Love Is a Song

Silhouettes of Dickens' characters are pictured in red, green, and white on a silver glass bell. Caption: "Christmas is a song of love for every heart to sing" and "1983."

Silver Glass Bell, 2½" tall
450QX223-9, $4.50 ☐

Love

White porcelain heart with embossed design of holly and berries frames a plump red heart hanging in its center which carries caption lettered in gold. A red satin ribbon is attached for hanging. Caption: "Love 1983."

Porcelain, 3⅛" tall
1300QX422-7, $13.00 ☐

Love

Hearts and greenery are reproduced from original needlepoint worked in sampler style. This design is also in the new Classic shape. Caption: "Love, the spirit which enhances all the seasons of our lives" and "Christmas 1983."

Classic Shape, 3¼" diam.
600QX310-9, $6.00 ☐

Love

Woodland snowscene pictures holiday travelers in a horse-driven sled. Caption: "Love makes each day a joy, each moment a memory" and "Christmas 1983."

Light Green Glass, 3¼" diam.
450QX207-9, $4.50 ☐

Teacher, First Christmas Together, Friendship, Love, Mother

Twenty-Fifth Christmas Together, Teacher, Friendship, New Home, Tenth Christmas Together

Clothespin Soldier — Second Edition

American Revolutionary clothespin soldier is beating his bass drum with arms that actually move.

Handcrafted, 2 7/16" tall
500QX402-9, $5.00 ☐

Rocking Horse — Third Edition

The third "trusty steed" in the series is russet in color, has blue saddle and bridle, tail of real ecru yarn, and green rocker dated "1983."

Handcrafted, 2 7/8" tall
1000QX417-7, $10.00 ☐

Frosty Friends — Fourth Edition

An Eskimo child and white baby seal covered with flocking are playing on a clear, freeform block of ice. Caption: "Merry Christmas 1983."

Handcrafted, 1 59/64" tall
800QX400-7, $8.00 ☐

Thimble — Sixth Edition

A merry elf is enjoying a cherry-topped ice cream treat served in a thimble.

Handcrafted, 1 15/16" tall
500QX401-7, $5.00 ☐

Tin Locomotive — Second Edition

An early locomotive lithographed in red and green and trimmed in gold features wheels that actually turn. Dated 1983.

Pressed Tin, 3" tall
1300QX404-9, $13.00 ☐

Collectible Series: Clothespin Soldier-Second Edition; Rocking Horse-Third Edition; Frosty Friends-Fourth Edition; Thimble Elf-Sixth Edition; Tin Locomotive-Second Edition

New Collectible Series: Porcelain Teddy Bear-First Edition

THE 1984 COLLECTION

The 1984 Hallmark Keepsake Collection offered tremendous excitement and expansion that included four new Collectible Series (Twelve Days of Christmas, Art Masterpiece, Wooden Toy and Nostalgic Houses and Shops); two new Friendship captions (Gratitude and Baby-sitter); timely designs inspired by the '84 Olympics (Marathon Santa) and the national elections (Uncle Sam); and a new property, Katybeth. Smaller sized ball ornaments were introduced, new handcrafted juvenile caps appeared on selected satin ornaments, and a new decorating process that included printing directly on the glass ball ornaments.

The 1984 Christmas season saw the last of The Bellringer series with Elfin Artist, and the first musical ornaments in the Keepsake line. "Holiday Magic Lighted Ornaments," a unique Hallmark innovation, debuted as did the first announced limited edition ornament, Classical Angel. Produced in an edition size of only 24,700, it was one of the most sought after items of the year.

Commemoratives

Baby's First Christmas
A holiday parade of animals, led by a baby in a sled, circles the ornament. Caption: "A Baby is...happiness, pleasure, a gift from above...a wonderful, magical treasure of love. Baby's First Christmas 1984." Melody: "Babes in Toyland"

Musical, Classic Shape, 4¼" tall
1600QX904-1, $16.00 ☐

Baby's First Christmas
A finely detailed teddy bear races downhill on an old-fashioned wooden-look sled bearing gifts. Caption: "1984 Baby's First Christmas."

Handcrafted, 3½" wide
1400QX438-1. $14.00 ☐

Baby's First Christmas
A snowy white fabric photoholder with dainty, embroidered holly sprigs at the top. Borders are fashioned of delicate, ruffled eyelet laced with pale green ribbon. Caption: "Baby's First Christmas. A Baby is a special dream come true. 1984."

Fabric, 3¼" diam.
700QX300-1, $7.00 ☐

Baby's First Christmas
Etched teddy bear holds a stocking filled with toys. Caption is accented with gold foil stamping: "1984 Baby's First Christmas."

Acyrlic, 3¾" tall
600QX340-1, $6.00 ☐

Baby's First Christmas: Musical, Handcrafted

Baby's First Christmas: Photoholder

Baby's First Christmas: Acrylic

Baby's First Christmas: Boy, Girl; Baby's Second Christmas, Child's Third Christmas

Baby's First Christmas—Boy
A bear drives a train filled with Christmas toys while a handcrafted mouse stands on top of the ornament. Caption: "A Baby Boy is a bundle of pleasure to fill every day with love beyond measure. Baby's First Christmas 1984."

White Satin, 2⅞" diam.
450QX240-4, $4.50 ☐

Baby's First Christmas—Girl
A handcrafted mouse appears atop a festive parade of happy little girls and Christmas toys. Caption: "A Baby Girl is love that grows in the warmth of caring hearts. Baby's First Christmas 1984."

Cream Satin, 2⅞" diam
450QX240-1, $4.50 ☐

Baby's Second Christmas
A golden crown caps the scene of Pooh Bear sharing Christmas with his friends. Caption: "Children and Christmas are joys that go together. Baby's Second Christmas 1984."

White Satin, 2⅞" diam.
450QX241-1. $4.50 ☐

Child's Third Christmas
A group of teddy bears decorate for Christmas on this satin ball topped with a handcrafted mouse. Caption: "A Child's Third Christmas. Christmas is a time for fun and wonderful surprises! 1984."

Ecru Satin, 2⅞" diam.
450QX261-1, $4.50 ☐

Grandchild's First Christmas
Flocked white lamb with red fabric ribbon around its neck balances on a colorful pull toy. At the lamb's feet are a baby rattle and a ball dated "1984." Caption: "Grandchild's First Christmas."

Handcrafted, 3⅜" tall
1100QX460-1, $11.00 ☐

Grandchild's First Christmas
A spring green satin ball provides the background for a unique "torn paper" scene of Santa loading toys into his bag. Ornament is capped with a handcrafted mouse. Caption: "A Baby makes Christmas delightfully bright. Grandchild's First Christms 1984."

Green Satin, 2⅞" diam.
450QX257-4,$4.50 ☐

Godchild
Elf-like children paint the holly berries red for the holidays. Caption: "Merry Christmas, Godchild 1984."

Gold Glass, 3" diam.
450QX242-1, $4.50 ☐

Grandchild's First Christmas: Handcrafted, Satin Ball; Godchild

Grandson, Granddaughter, Grandparents, Grandmother

Father, Mother

Mother and Dad, Sister, Daughter, Son

The Miracle of Love, First Christmas Together

Grandson
A polar bear family shares Christmas fun. Caption: "A Grandson has a wonderful way of adding love to every day. Christmas 1984."
Blue Glass, 3" diam.
450QX242-4, $4.50 ☐

Granddaughter
A festive holdiay sampler is reproduced from original stitchery. Caption: "A Granddaughter is warmth, hope and promise. Christmas 1984."
Green Glass, 2⅞" diam.
450QX243-1, $4.50 ☐

Grandparents
A contemporary snow scene, reproduced from original stitchery, provides the perfect setting for the caption: "Grandparents ... wherever they are, there is love. Christmas 1984."
French Blue Glass, 2⅞" diam.
450QX256-1, $4.50 ☐

Grandmother
Lovely, muted pastel flowers frame a holiday tribute to Grandmother. Caption: "There's a special kind of beauty in a Grandmother's special love. Christmas 1984."
Light Blue Glass, 2⅞" diam.
450QX244-1, $4.50 ☐

Father
The wonderful sounds of Christmas are symbolized by holly and musical instruments etched across the top. Stamped in gold foil, the caption reads, "A Father has a special gift of giving of himself. Christmas 1984."
Acrylic, 3¼" wide
600QX257-1, $6.00 ☐

Mother
Etched fir branches tied with a ribbon are accented by the silver foil-stamped caption: "A Mother has a beautiful way of adding love to every day. 1984."
Acrylic, 3¼" wide
600QX343-4, $6.00 ☐

Mother and Dad
Gold highlights the classic Christmas design motifs that adorn this delicate bone china bell tied with red ribbon. Caption: "Mother and Dad. Christmas 1984."
Bone China, 3" tall
650QX258-1, $6.50 ☐

Sister
A bright basket of poinsettias rests against a dark blue background, framed in red on a delicate bone china bell. Caption: "For a wonderful Sister. Christmas 1984."
Bone China, 3" tall
650QX259-4, $6.50 ☐

First Christmas Together: Musical, Brushed Brass, Cameo, Silver Glass

Daughter
Bright holiday flowers and the striking contrast of green and gold complement the loving caption: "A Daughter is joy that grows deeper, pride that grows stronger, love that touches your heart every day. Christmas 1984."
Gold Glass, 3" diam.
450QX244-4, $4.50 ☐

Son
Whimsical Christmas designs form letters that spell "Merry Christmas." Caption: "For a wonderful Son. Christmas 1984."
White Glass, 3" diam.
450QX243-4, $4.50 ☐

The Miracle of Love
Romantic acrylic heart etched with festive ribbon and holly design. Caption is gold foil stamped: "Love...a miracle of the heart. Christmas 1984."
Acrylic, 4" tall
600QX342-4, $6.00 ☐

First Christmas Together
A delicately etched design shows two doves perched on a holly branch. The caption, stamped with silver foil, says, "First Christmas Together 1984."
Acrylic, 3⅝" diam
600QX342-1, $6.00 ☐

First Christmas Together
The love of a first Christmas together is captured in the melody of "Lara's Theme" while reindeer prance across the deep blue background. Caption: "First Christmas Together 1984." Melody: "Lara's Theme"
Musical, Classic Shape, 4" tall
1600QX904-4, $16.00 ☐

First Christmas Together
Brushed brass oval locket opens to hold two photos and comes with its own felt pouch. Hanger allows open or closed display on your tree. The caption is engraved on the cover and framed by embossed hearts. Caption: "First Christmas Together 1984."
Brushed Brass, 2½" tall
1500QX436-4, $15.00 ☐

First Christmas Together
An elegant couple, carved in ivory relief, waltz across a dark blue background. Caption: "Each moment spent together is a special celebration. First Christmas Together 1984."
Cameo, 3¼" diam.
750QX340-4, $7.50 ☐

First Christmas Together
Silver ball is surrounded by a contemporary pattern of holiday birds, flowers and greenery. Caption: "Love...a joy for all seasons. First Christmas Together 1984."
Silver Glass, 3" diam.
450QX245-1, $4.50 ☐

Heartful of Love

A bone china puffed heart is decorated with a romantic design of pink, red and yellow roses. The date "1984" appears on one side and a banner across the other bears the caption: "Love...the most beautiful treasure of Christmas."

Bone China, 3¾" wide
1000QX443-4, $10.00 ☐

Love...the Spirit of Christmas

The shiny black band and the bright Christmas fruit and flower design give this chrome glass ball the appearance of fine lacquer boxes. Caption: "Love, which is the spirit and the heart of Christmas, blossoms all year through. 1984."

Chrome Glass, 2⅞" diam.
450QX247-4, $4.50 ☐

Love

Classic mimes share thoughts of love against a bright red background. Caption: "Love can say the special things that words alone cannot. Christmas 1984."

Chrome Glass, 2⅞" diam.
450QX255-4, $4.50 ☐

Ten Years Together

A white bone china bell features a lovely, frosty blue winter scene inside an oval. Tied in blue fabric ribbon, the bell is captioned, "Ten Years Together. Christmas 1984."

Bone China, 3" tall
650QX258-4, $6.50 ☐

Twenty-Five Years Together

A bone china bell with silver hanging cord pictures an ornate gold and silver sleigh filled with holiday gifts. Caption: "Twenty-Five Years Together. Christmas 1984."

Bone China, 3" tall
650QX259-1, $6.50 ☐

Gratitude

Acrylic teardrop shape is etched with a cheery design of ribbon and sleigh bells. Caption is applied with silver foil stamping. Caption: "The spirit of Christmas lives in every heart that gives."

Acrylic, 4½" tall
600QX344-4, $6.00 ☐

The Fun of Friendship

Scallops decorate the rim of an acrylic bell etched with a charming portrait of two Arctic pals. Silver foil-stamped caption reads, "A friend is a partner in life's merry moments. 1984."

Acrylic, 3¾" tall
600QX343-1, $6.00 ☐

Heartful of Love, Love...the Spirit of Christmas, Love

Ten Years Together, Twenty-Five Years Together

Gratitude, The Fun of Friendship

Friendship
Carolers sing amidst the gentle fall of snowflakes. Set in a red border, the caption reads, "Let us sing a Christmas song of friendship, joy and cheer. 1984."

Blue-Green Glass, $2\frac{7}{8}$" diam
450QX248-1, $4.50 ☐

A Gift of Friendship
Muffin and her white kitten rest on a light peach glass ball. Caption: "Friendship is the happiest gift of all!"

Peach Glass, 3" diam.
450QX260-4, $4.50 ☐

New Home
Pearl blue glass forms the background for a village holiday snow scene. Caption: "Home is where the heart is and a new home always seems the happiest of places, for it is filled with all your dreams. Christmas 1984."

Pearl Blue Glass, $2\frac{7}{8}$" diam.
450QX245-4, $4.50 ☐

From Our Home to Yours
Sampler design, reproduced from original stitchery, shows an inviting home with family enjoying the snow. Caption: "The spirit of Christmas adorns a home with love. Christmas 1984."

Green Glass, $2\frac{7}{8}$" diam.
450QX248-4, $4.50 ☐

Teacher
Whimsical elves deliver a big red apple to teacher. Caption: "1984 Merry Christmas, Teacher."

White Glass, 3" diam.
450QX249-1, $4.50 ☐

Baby-sitter
A charming group of mice depict the fun of Christmas and the closeness shared by children and baby-sitter. Caption: "Thank heaven for Baby-sitters like you."

Green Glass, 3" diam.
450QX253-1, $4.50 ☐

Friendship, A Gift of Friendship, New Home

From Our House to Yours, Teacher, Baby-sitter

Property Ornaments

Betsey Clark Angel
Betsey Clark's hand-painted, fine porcelain angel is dressed in a soft pink dress and white pinafore. The angel plays a holiday song on her mandolin.

Hand-Painted Porcelain, 3½″ tall
900QX462-4, $9.00 ☐

Katybeth
Katybeth is a new Hallmark property in the Keepsake line in 1984. Holding a friendly star, this freckled-faced angel wears a golden halo...a little off-center.

Hand-Painted Porcelain, 2¼″ tall
900QX463-1, $9.00 ☐

PEANUTS ®
SNOOPY ® watches as WOODSTOCK and friends build a gallery of snowmen. SNOOPY'S ® red banner says, "Merry Christmas." Ornament is dated "1984."

Light Blue Soft Sheen Satin, 2⅞″ diam.
450QX252-1, $4.50 ☐

DISNEY
The Disney gang — Mickey, Minnie, Donald, Daisy and Pluto — sends holiday greetings. Caption: "Friends put the merry in Christmas. 1984."

White Glass, 2⅞″ diam.
450QX250-4, $4.50 ☐

The MUPPETS™
KERMIT™, framed by a Christmas wreath, dons a Santa cap to wish us, "Hoppy, Hoppy Holidays!" MISS PIGGY™, framed by a heart-shaped wreath, says, "Merry Kissmas!"

Chrome Glass, 2⅞″ diam.
450QX251-4, $4.50 ☐

Norman Rockwell
This gold ball shows three famous paintings from the Hallmark Collection of Norman Rockwell artwork. Each panel depicts the artist's intepretation of Dickens Christmas characters. Caption: "Good friends, good times, good health, good cheer and happy days throughout the year. From the Norman Rockwell Collection 1984."

Gold Glass, 2⅞″ diam.
450QX251-1, $4.50 ☐

Currier & Ives
Always a favorite, Currier & Ives artwork is carefully reproduced on white blown glass. Caption: "American Winter Scenes, Evening, Christmas 1984."

White Glass, 2⅞″ diam.
450QX250-1, $4.50 ☐

Betsey Clark, Katybeth, PEANUTS®, DISNEY

MUPPETS™, Norman Rockwell, Currier & Ives, Shirt Tales™

Shirt Tales™

The Shirt Tales™ join in a merry snowball fight. Ball is capped with a golden crown. Caption: "Joy in the air, good time to share — Christmas, Christmas everywhere."

Aqua-Blue Satin, 2⅞" diam.
450QX252-4, $4.50 ☐

SNOOPY® and WOODSTOCK

Everyone's favorite beagle takes to the slopes with his faithful pal WOODSTOCK leading the way. But it's cold outside, so SNOOPY® wears a warm fabric scarf.

Handcrafted, 4¼" wide
750QX439-1, $7.50 ☐

Muffin

You'll always know Muffin by the red knitted cap she wears everywhere she goes. She's bringing a holiday gift to her friend Kit.

Handcrafted, 2¾" tall
550QX442-1, $5.50 ☐

Kit

Muffin's special friend Kit is known for his green cap. He brings a candy cane to sweeten your Christmas. Kit and Muffin make a perfect pair on the tree.

Handcrafted, 2¾" tall
550QX453-4, $5.50 ☐

Traditional Ornaments

White Christmas

The hustle and bustle of Christmas time is shown in a wintry town square of yesteryear. Caption: "At Christmas time, love shines in every smile, glows in every heart." Melody: "White Christmas."

Musical, Classic Shape, 4½" tall
1600QX905-1, $16.00 ☐

Twelve Days of Christmas

This musical ornament was originally part of Hallmark's Musical Decoration line. In 1984 it was re-introduced as a Keepsake Ornament. Melody: "The Twelve Days of Christmas."

Musical, Handcrafted, 3¾" tall
1500QX415-9, $15.00 ☐

Gift of Music

A colorfully dressed, bearded elf ties his holiday gift with red ribbon. The label on the blue wrapped gift says, "Jolly Holidays!" Melody: "Jingle Bells."

Musical, Handcrafted, 3" tall
1500QX451-1, $15.00 ☐

SNOOPY®, and WOODSTOCK, Muffin, Kit

White Christmas, Twelve Days of Christmas, Gift of Music

Amanda
Dressed in ruffled frock and bonnet of bright green fabric, Amanda is ready for a Christmas party. Her face and hands are fashioned of fine porcelain and painted by hand.

Fabric, Hand-Painted Porcelain, 4¾″ tall
900QX432-1, $9.00 ☐

Holiday Jester
Looking as if he may have played to royal audiences, this jester wears the traditional black and white costume with gold shoes. His arms and legs are movable.

Handcrafted, 5¼″ tall
1100QX437-4, $11.00 ☐

Uncle Sam
A pressed tin Uncle Sam, holding a teddy bear and flags, wears an "84" badge to remind us of that Presidential election year.

Pressed Tin, 5″ tall
600QX449-1, $6.00 ☐

Chickadee
Hand-painted porcelain chickadee brings a cluster of mistletoe to your tree. A metal clip keeps the bird perched on the branch.

Hand-Painted Porcelain, 3¼″ wide
600QX451-4, $6.00 ☐

Cuckoo Clock
"Merry Christmas" is the "time" etched on the brass face of this intricately detailed clock that comes complete with pinecone pendulums. Santa's face decorates the top and a reindeer adorns the bottom.

Handcrafted, 3¼″ tall
1000QX455-1, $10.00 ☐

Alpine Elf
Holiday messages echo through the Alps when this elf plays his long carved horn.

Handcrafted, 3½″ wide
600QX452-1, $6.00 ☐

Nostalgic Sled
This classic-style sled evokes memories of childhood fun. Sled has real string rope and metal runners. Caption: "Season's Greetings."

Handcrafted, 3½″ wide
600QX442-4, $6.00 ☐

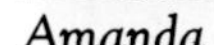

Amanda

Holiday Jester, Uncle Sam

Chickadee, Cuckoo Clock, Alpine Elf, Nostalgic Sled

Santa Sulky Driver
Santa races along in his etched brass rig that displays a "Season's Greetings" banner.

Etched Brass, 1¾" tall
900QX436-1, $9.00 ☐

Old Fashioned Rocking Horse
A new look for the Keepsake line, this ornament features a finely etched rocking horse embedded in acrylic.

Brass, Acrylic, 3¼" diam.
750QX346-4, $7.50 ☐

Madonna and Child
The Madonna cradles the Holy Child as a dove of peace watches in this loving scene etched in acrylic. The gold foil-stamped caption reads, "All is calm, all is bright..."

Acrylic, 4" tall
600QX344-1, $6.00 ☐

Holiday Friendship
This panorama peek-through ball depicts the friendship shared by a little boy and girl. Both hide gifts as they wave to each other through a frosty window.

Peek-Through Ball, 3¼" diam.
1300QX445-1, $13.00 ☐

Peace on Earth
Oval red cameo shows a beautiful old-world angel in ivory relief playing a harp. Caption: "Peace on Earth."

Cameo, 3" tall
750QX341-4, $7.50 ☐

A Savior is Born
A Nativity scene with holiday flowers brings the most important message of the season: "For unto you is born this day in the City of David a Savior which is Christ the Lord. Luke 2:11."

Purple Glass, 2⅞" diam.
450QX254-1, $4.50 ☐

Holiday Starburst
Holiday ribbons wrap around the silver starburst seen inside this clear glass ball. The caption, "Christmas 1984" is printed in gold.

Clear Glass, 2⅞" diam.
500QX253-4, $5.00 ☐

Santa Sulky Driver, Rocking Horse, Madonna and Child

Holiday Friendship, Peace on Earth, A Savior is Born, Holiday Starburst

Santa
Santa rides a reindeer over lush green hillsides filled with blooming flowers.
Hand-Embroidered Fabric, 4″ tall
750QX458-4, $7.50 ☐

Needlepoint Wreath
The delicate intricacy of needlepoint is beautifully displayed in this handmade wreath of bright holiday poinsettias.
Needlepoint-Fabric, 3½″ diam.
650QX459-4, $6.50 ☐

Christmas Memories Photoholder
A striking array of holiday fabrics forms a wreath fashioned to display a special Christmas photo. Caption: "Christmas is a remembering time 1984."
Fabric, 3″ diam.
650QX300-4, $6.50 ☐

Embroidered Heart
Reissue from 1983. (See 1983 Annual Collection.)
Hand-Embroidered Fabric, 4¾″ tall
650QX421-7, $6.50

Embroidered Stocking
Reissue from 1983. (See 1983 Annual Collection.)
Hand-Embroidered Fabric, 3¼″ tall
650QX479-6, $6.50

Holiday Humor

Bell Ringer Squirrel
A handcrafted squirrel swinging from an acorn forms the unique clapper in this clear glass bell.
Glass, Handcrafted, 4″ tall
1000QX443-1, $10.00 ☐

Raccoon's Christmas
Handcrafted raccoon is at home in his snow-covered tree house. Both he and his little neighbor have hung their Christmas stockings.
Handcrafted, 2¾″ tall
900QX447-4, $9.00 ☐

Three Kittens in a Mitten
Three kittens — black, tan, and gold — have found themselves in a dilemma. A real knitted red and green mitten.
Handcrafted, 3½″ tall
800QX431-1. $8.00 ☐

Marathon Santa
Santa carries a torch dated "1984." He's a gold medalist on December 25!
Handcrafted, 2¼″ tall
800QX456-4, $8.00 ☐

Santa, Needlepoint Wreath, Christmas Memories Photoholder

Bell Ringer Squirrel, Raccoon's Christmas, Three Kittens in a Mitten, Marathon Santa

Santa Star
A shining example of Santa! He's designed in the shape of a five-pointed star.

Handcrafted, 3½" tall
550QX450-4,$5.50 ☐

Snowmobile Santa
Santa goes out in his shiny new snowmobile. He loves the ride, but he has reasurred his reindeer that he won't be snowmobiling on Christmas Eve!

Handcrafted, 2¾" wide
650QX431-4, $6.50 ☐

Snowshoe Penguin
This neighbor of Santa's has set out in his showshoes to deliver his own Christmas gift. His cap has a real pom-pom.

Handcrafted, 3" tall
650QX453-1, $6.50 ☐

Christmas Owl
A wise little owl, wearing Santa's hat, watches from a clear acrylic moon. His Christmas stocking, made to fit his foot, hangs from the moon's tip.

Handcrafted, Acrylic, 3¾" tall
600QX444-1, $6.00 ☐

Musical Angel
This little angel has a unique view of Christmas, but even her position won't stop her from playing a heavenly tune. The banner hanging from her brass horn is stamped with the caption: "Noel."

Handcrafted, 1¼" tall
550QX434-4, $5.50 ☐

Napping Mouse
This little mouse is not "stirring," he's napping in a walnut shell while holding tightly to his "teddy mouse." The blanket is a red and white dotted fabric ribbon.

Handcrafted, 1¾" tall
550QX435-1, $5.50 ☐

Roller Skating Rabbit
The red wheels actually turn on the green and white roller skate shoe in which the white bunny is nestled for a holiday "spin."

Handcrafted, 2½" wide
500QX457-1, $5.00 ☐

Frisbee® Puppy
This playful puppy makes a spectacular leap and catches the "Merry Christmas" Frisbee®. He wears a green fabric bow for the holidays.

Handcrafted, 2¾" tall
500QX444-4, $5.00 ☐

Santa Star, Snowmobile Santa, Snowshoe Penguin, Christmas Owl

Musical Angel, Napping Mouse, Roller Skating Rabbit, Frisbee® Puppy

Reindeer Racetrack
The race has started and the reindeer runners are off! Santa, in the viewing crowd, encourages his friends with a famous line from Clement C. Moore's "Night Before Christmas": "On, Comet! On, Cupid! On, Donder! On, Blitzen!"

Red Glass, 3″ diam.
450QX254-4, $4.50 ☐

A Christmas Prayer
Mary Hamilton's charming angels frolic in the clouds, chasing stars. Ball is capped with a golden crown. Caption: "Little prayer be on your way...bless our friends on Christmas Day."

Blue Sheen Satin, 2⅞″ diam.
450QX246-1, $4.50 ☐

Flights of Fantasy
Elves take flight on the backs of beautiful birds flying in the moonlight on this fanciful holiday ball. A ribbon banner says, "Christmas 1984."

Blue Glass, 2⅞″ diam.
450QX256-4, $4.50 ☐

Polar Bear Drummer
This white polar bear drums up some holiday spirit while keeping warm with a plaid fabric scarf.

Handcrafted, 2¼″ tall
450QX430-1, $4.50 ☐

Santa Mouse
Mister Mouse dresses as Santa with a jacket and cap and furry plush beard.

Handcrafted, 2″ tall
450QX433-4, $4.50 ☐

Snowy Seal
This soft, flocked white seal with dark eyes is dressed for the holidays in a red fabric ribbon.

Handcrafted, 1½″ wide
400QX450-1, $4.00 ☐

Fortune Cookie Elf
An elf paints your fortune for a holiday fortune cookie. Caption: "May your Christmas be merry."

Handcrafted, 2½″ tall
450Q452-4, $4.50 ☐

Peppermint 1984
The year 1984 in peppermint candy. Two birds enjoy the view from atop the number nine.

Handcrafted, 2¾″ wide
450Q456-1, $4.50 ☐

Reindeer Racetrack, A Christmas Prayer, Flights of Fantasy, Polar Bear Drummer

Santa Mouse, Snowy Seal, Fortune Cookie Elf, Peppermint 1984

Mountain Climbing Santa

Reissue from 1983. (See 1983 Annual Collection.)

Handcrafted, 2½″ tall
650QX407-7, $6.50

Limited Edition

Classical Angel

Limited to an edition size of 24,700 pieces, this elegant, hand-painted porcelain angel is Hallmark's first announced limited edition ornament. She stands five inches tall and comes with her own wood display stand. Dressed in a flowing dress of pink, golden-yellow and white, she carries a chain of brass bells. Dated "1984."

Hand-Painted Porcelain, 5″ tall
2750QX459-1., $27.50 ☐

Collectible Series

Nostalgic Houses and Shops—First Edition

This elegant "Victorian Dollhouse," scaled one inch to one foot, is perfect for both ornament and dollhouse collectors. The fully decorated interior comes complete with wallpaper, furniture, a Christmas tree and even a miniature dollhouse.

Handcrafted, 3¼″ tall
1300QX448-1, $13.00 ☐

Wood Childhood Ornaments—First Edition

Hand-painted "Wooden Lamb" evokes memories of Christmas past. Wheels that turn and a red fabric bow at the neck add wonderful touches of authenticity.

Wood, Handcrafted, 2¼″ tall
650QX439-4, $6.50 ☐

Classical Angel

Nostalgic Houses and Shops, Wood Childhood Ornaments

The Twelve Days of Christmas—First Edition
The popular old Christmas song is immortalized on scalloped acrylic. An etched partridge and pear tree depict the first of the days and the gold-foil stamped caption reads, "The Twelve Days of Christmas 1984...and a partridge in a pear tree."
Acrylic, 3" tall
600QX348-4, $6.00 ☐

Art Masterpiece—First Edition
This series brings timeless works of art into your home. The first ornament offers a classic oil painting reproduced on padded satin. Caption: "Giuliano Bugiardini, 'Madonna and Child and St. John,' (ca. 1505) The Nelson-Atkins Museum of Art, Kansas City, Missouri, (Nelson Fund)."
Bezeled Satin, 2¾" diam.
650QX349-4, $6.50 ☐

Porcelain Bear—Second Edition
An adorable "Cinnamon Bear," fashioned in hand-painted porcelain, holds a gold jingle bell with red bow.
Hand-Painted Porcelain, 2½" tall
700QX454-1, $7.00 ☐

Tin Locomotive—Third Edition
Number three in the pressed Tin Locomotive Series is an antique design with movable wheels; the muted colors are red, soft blue, lavender and steel. Dated "1984."
Pressed Tin, 2½" tall
1400QX440-4, $14.00 ☐

Clothespin Soldier — Third Edition
Red and black uniformed Canadian Mountie proudly bears a holiday flag.
Handcrafted, 2½" tall
500QX447-1, $5.00 ☐

Holiday Wildlife—Third Edition
A pair of graceful Ring-Necked Pheasants are pictured against a snow-covered setting on a porcelain-look inset framed in wood. Caption: "Ring-Necked Pheasant, Phasianus Torquatus, Third in a series, Wildlife Collection, Christmas 1984."
Handcrafted, 3" diam.
725QX347-4, $7.25 ☐

Twelve Days of Christmas, Art Masterpiece, Porcelain Bear

Tin Locomotive, Clothespin Soldier, Holiday Wildlife

Rocking Horse—Fourth Edition
Racing into the holiday season is the fourth of the "Rocking Horse" series. The blue and red saddle and rockers provide a colorful contrast to this white and black speckled appaloosa with gray mane and flying yarn tail. Dated "1984."

Handcrafted, 4″ wide
1000QX435-4, $10.00 ☐

Frosty Friends—Fifth Edition
The little Eskimo has gone ice fishing with his penguin pal. The catch of the day is a Christmas gift, all wrapped and dated "1984."

Handcrafted, 2½″ tall
800QX437-1, $8.00 ☐

Norman Rockwell—Fifth Edition
Rockwell's famous *Caught Napping* is the subject of this delicate cameo. Santa peeks from behind a high-backed chair at two pajama-clad children who tried their best to stay awake for his visit. The background is deep blue with white relief. Caption: "Caught Napping, Fifth in a Series, The Norman Rockwell Collection, Christmas 1984."

Cameo, 3″ diam.
750QX341-1, $7.50 ☐

Here Comes Santa—Sixth Edition
Santa's "free delivery" service carries a load of Christmas trees as its cargo. Called "Santa's Deliveries," this ornament has wheels that actually turn. License plate, "1984."

Handcrafted, 3¼″ tall
1300QX432-4, $13.00 ☐

The Bellringer—Sixth and Final Edition
The "Elfin Artist," swinging on the outside of a white, fine porcelain bell, has painted his message in red: "Christmas 1984."

Porcelain, 3½″ tall
1500QX438-4, $15.00 ☐

Thimble—Seventh Edition
Heavenly blue-gowned angel holds a shiny thimble full of sparkling acrylic stars.

Handcrafted, 1¾″ tall
500QX430-4, $5.00 ☐

Betsey Clark—Twelfth Edition
Artist Betsey Clark's little waifs decorate their home for the holidays. Caption: "Days are merry, hearts are light, and all the world's a lovely sight. Chrismas 1984."

White Frosted Glass, 3¼″ diam.
500QX249-4, $5.00 ☐

Rocking Horse, Frosty Friends, Norman Rockwell

Here Comes Santa, Bellringer, Thimble, Betsey Clark

THE 1985 COLLECTION

The 1985 Keepsake Ornament line continued Hallmark's attempts to design ornaments that meet collectors' needs. Collectors expressed a definite interest in ornaments that look homemade and are fashioned of natural materials such as wood and fabric. To respond to this demand, Hallmark offered two special coordinated groups of five ornaments each.

The "Country Christmas Collection" included ornaments created of wood or porcelain, or fashioned in the look of hand-carved wood. The carefully researched designs captured a nostalgic country flavor. The "Heirloom Christmas Collection" used satin, lace, ribbon and intricate crochet work to bring back the romance of another era. These elegant designs were inspired by popular, turn-of-the-century styles, with some even including rose-scented sachets.

Limited Edition and Collectible Series ornaments are also favorites with collectors. The '85 line featured two new series and the second limited edition Keepsake, a fine porcelain angel called "Heavenly Trumpeter" produced in an edition size of 24,700 pieces. The two new series were "Windows of the World," showing children from all around the globe celebrating Christmas, and "Miniature Creche," offering a new Nativity scene fashioned of different materials each year.

Three properties, FRAGGLE ROCK™, Rainbow Brite™, and Hugga Bunch made their debut this year, as did an ornament designed especially for Niece. Among the new formats were a satin-covered container with a card tucked inside for personalization, and an ornament made of stained glass.

Commemoratives

Baby's First Christmas
A beautiful embroidered satin baby block, bordered in lace, plays a lullaby for Baby. The ABC, four-sided caption reads, "A Baby's 1st Christmas 1985." Melody: "Schubert's Lullaby."

Musical, Fabric, 3¼″ tall
1600QX499-5, $16.00 ☐

Baby's First Christmas
Baby's out for a ride to deliver a special Christmas gift. This lace-trimmed, rattan-look stroller with real fabric bow and pillow was inspired by a turn-of-the-century mail-order catalog and is built to scale. Caption: "Baby's First Christmas 1985."

Handcrafted, 3¾″ tall
1500QX499-2, $15.00 ☐

Baby Locket
Textured brass locket has a space for Baby's photo and for personalizing. The caption, "Baby," is decorated with embossed toys.

Textured Brass, 2¼″ diam.
1600QX401-2, $16.00 ☐

Baby's First Christmas
An acrylic baby cup, brimming with toys, is captioned, "Baby's First Christmas 1985" in stamped silver foil.

Acrylic, 3¾″ tall
575QX370-2, $5.75 ☐

Baby's First Christmas: Musical, Handcrafted

Baby Locket, Baby's First Christmas: Acrylic

Baby's First Christmas
This hand-embroidered tree is just Baby's size! It's decorated with ribbon and lace and is captioned, "1985 Baby's 1st Christmas."

Embroidered Fabric, 4½" tall
700QX478-2, $7.00 ☐

Baby's First Christmas
Dressed in yellow, Baby is delighted by the Christmas toys shown around the center of this green satin ball. Ornament is topped with a handcrafted mouse. Caption: "A Baby keeps the season bright and warms the heart with sweet delight. Baby's First Christmas 1985."

Green Soft-Sheen Satin, 2⅞" diam.
500QX260-2, $5.00 ☐

Baby's Second Christmas
An adorable teddy bear rides a stick pony that has a plush mane and fabric reins. Teddy's shirt is captioned, "Baby's Second Christmas 1985."

Handcrafted, 3½" tall
600QX478-5, $6.00 ☐

Child's Third Christmas
A brown flocked teddy bear has found a home in a red and white sneaker laced with a real shoestring. Sneaker is bordered with the caption: "A Child's Third Christmas '85."

Handcrafted, 2¼" tall
600QX475-5, $6.00 ☐

Grandchild's First Christmas
The elves are busily making Christmas toys on this ecru ball topped with a handcrafted mouse. Sitting on Santa's knee, the adorable little baby can't wait to hug his new teddy bear. The caption reads, "Grandchild's First Christmas 1985."

Ecru Satin, 2⅞" diam.
500QX260-5, $5.00 ☐

Grandchild's First Christmas
White hand-knitted bootie with ribbon trim is filled with toys Baby will love. Caption: "Grandchild's First Christmas 1985."

Handcrafted, 3¼" tall
1100QX495-5, $11.00 ☐

Baby's First Christmas: Fabric, Satin Ball; Baby's Second Christmas

Child's Third Christmas, Grandchild's First Christmas: Satin Ball, Handcrafted

Grandparents, Niece, Mother

Mother and Dad, Father, Sister, Daughter

Godchild, Son

Grandmother, Grandson, Granddaughter

Grandparents
A white poinsettia appears against a rich garnet background to create a unique lacquer-look that is new to the Keepsake Ornament line. Framed in brass, the design is accented with gold for an extra-festive touch. Caption: "Grandparents have beautiful ways of adding love to the holidays. Christmas 1985."

Bezeled Lacquer-Look, 2¾" wide
700QX380-5, $7.00 ☐

Niece
A new and sure-to-be-popular caption. Stamped in silver foil on an acrylic teardrop is the sentiment: "A Niece fills hearts with a special kind of love. Christmas 1985."

Acrylic, 3¾" tall
575QX520-5, $5.75 ☐

Mother
Clear acrylic raindrop, framed in a golden ring, brings a tribute to Mother. The gold foil-stamped caption reads, "Mother is the heart of our happiest holiday memories. Christmas 1985."

Acrylic, 3⅜" tall
675QX372-2, $6.75 ☐

Mother and Dad
Snowy white, fine porcelain bell has bas-relief paisley design. The trim, caption, tie cord and tassle are all coordinated in soft blue. Caption: "Mother and Dad. Christmas 1985."

Porcelain, 3" tall
775QX509-2, $7.75 ☐

Father
Filled with gifts and a Christmas tree, this old-fashioned sleigh is printed on hardwood with the look of hand painting. Caption: "A Father sees through the eyes of love and listens with his heart. Christmas 1985."

Wood, 3" diam.
650QX376-2, $6.50 ☐

Sister
This white porcelain bell, hanging from a red ribbon, has a cheerful heart and holly design that looks as if it were hand-painted especially for Sister. Caption: "For Sister with love. Christmas 1985."

Porcelain, 2¾" tall
725QX506-5, $7.25 ☐

Daughter
Framed in a wooden embroidery hoop tied with a delicately embroidered fabric ribbon, the design has the look of fine silk-screening. Caption: "A Daughter decorates the holidays with love. Christmas 1985."

Wood, 3¼" diam.
550QX503-2, $5.50 ☐

First Christmas Together Brass, Love at Christmas, First Christmas Together Acrylic

Godchild
This unique design has been taken from Hallmark's Antique Greeting Card Collection and reproduced on padded satin. The caption on the reverse side is stamped in gold foil. Caption: "A Godchild is a loving gift to treasure through the years. Christmas 1985."

Bezeled Satin, 2¾" Diam.
675QX380-2, $6.75 ☐

Son
An adorable terrier, with a fabric bow at his neck, fetches the message: "Merry Christmas, Son 1985."

Handcrafted, 2" tall
550QX502-5, $5.50 ☐

Grandmother
A nostalgic floral design decorates this transparent red, teardrop-shaped ball. The scroll banner bears the caption: "A Grandmother gives the gift of love. Christmas 1985."

Red Glass, 3" diam.
475QX262-5, $4.75 ☐

Grandson
A bright red, green and yellow antique train chugs around a green glass ball bringing Grandson a Christmas message. Caption: "A Grandson makes holiday joys shine even brighter! Christmas 1985."

Green Glass, 2⅞" diam.
475QX262-2, $4.75 ☐

Granddaughter
A contemporary American country look is achieved in the design of the vividly colored animals on the center of this ivory ball. Caption: "There's nothing like a Granddaughter to warm the world at Christmas. 1985."

Ivory Glass, 2⅞" diam.
475QX263-5, $4.75 ☐

First Christmas Together
Romantic embossed hearts surround the caption "First Christmas Together 1985" on the cover of this polished brass locket. With its special hanger, the locket can be displayed closed to show the cover or open to reveal your two photos inside. Locket comes with a special felt storage pouch.

Polished Brass, 2½" tall
1675QX400-5, $16.75 ☐

Love at Christmas
It's raining romantic red foil hearts on this heart of acrylic etched with the caption: "The spirit of Christmas is love."

Acrylic, 3¼" wide
575QX371-5, $5.75 ☐

First Christmas Together
On a clear acrylic oval, framed in brass, a graceful pair of etched doves carry a banner bearing the gold foil-stamped caption: "First Christmas Together 1985."

Acrylic, 3½" wide
675QX370-5, $6.75 ☐

First Christmas Together
A pale green bisque porcelain bell with scalloped, bas-relief design becomes a romantic symbol of love. The red porcelain, double-heart clapper bears the caption: "First Christmas Together 1985."

Porcelain, 2" tall
1300QX493-5, $13.00 ☐

Holiday Heart
Colorful flowers and holiday greenery decorate a white, fine porcelain puffed heart. The ornament is captioned with the word "Love" in bas-relief and topped with a white fabric tassel.

Porcelain, 2" tall
800QX498-2, $8.00 ☐

First Christmas Together
This design is a unique blend of old-fashioned charm and romance. The red heart is hand-woven inside a wooden frame decorated with a bright red fabric tassel. Caption: "1985 First Christmas Together."

Fabric, Wood, 2½" tall
800QX507-2, $8.00 ☐

Heart Full of Love
A lovely winter scene of snow-capped trees, accented by brightly colored cardinals and red berries, is printed on padded satin and framed with a chrome ring. Caption: "The world is full of beauty when hearts are full of love. Christmas 1985."

Bezeled Satin, 3" tall
675QX378-2, $6.75 ☐

First Christmas Together
Heart-shaped frames reveal romantic silhouette vignettes painted in shades of blue, green and red. Caption: "Love is a gift from heart to heart. First Christmas Together 1985."

Light Blue Glass, 2⅞" diam.
475QX261-2, $4.75 ☐

Twenty-Five Years Together
This miniature porcelain plate, a new format in 1985, is decorated with a gold, silver and blue holly wreath. The border caption on the front reads, "Twenty-Five Years Together." Back: "Christmas 1985." Plate stand included.

Porcelain, 3¼" diam.
800QX500-5, $8.00 ☐

First Christmas Porcelain Bell, Holiday Heart, First Christmas Fabric and Wood

Heart Full of Love, First Christmas Together Glass Ball, Twenty-Five Years Together

Friendship
A new format for 1985, this tasseled container, covered in rich Oriental red satin, is hand embroidered with a pine and snowflake design. A gift card for personalizing is tucked inside and the caption reads, "Christmas...a special time for friendship. 1985."

Embroidered Satin, 2" tall
775QX506-2, $7.75 ☐

Friendship
An early American village reflects the warmth of Christmas and of friendship. If you look carefully you'll see Santa standing in the middle of town. Artwork is printed on padded satin and framed with a chrome bezel. Caption: "Christmas ... season bright with friendship. 1985."

Bezeled Satin, 3" tall
675QX378-5, $6.75 ☐

From Our House to Yours
Holiday decorations in the windows of this beautifully detailed, handmade needlepoint house tell visiting neighbors that friendship and Christmas cheer are inside. The caption on red satin reads, "A happy home reflects the joy of Christmas all year round. 1985."

Needlepoint-Fabric, 4" tall
775QX520-2, $7.75 ☐

Teacher
A wise owl is ready for class as he perches on a slate board displaying the lesson, "Merry Christmas to a Grade A Teacher!" The owl's book has the title "School Days 1985." There is room for personalization on the back of the slate.

Handcrafted, 3" tall
600QX505-2, $6.00 ☐

With Appreciation
A lovely combination of silver and gold appears in this acrylic oval framed in brass. Stamped in silver foil, snowflakes surround the gold foil-stamped caption: "Christmas...a time when we think of those who have given us so much. 1985."

Acrylic, 3½" tall
675QX375-2, $6.75 ☐

Special Friends
Unique quadrafoil acrylic shape is the setting for this charming etching of a doll and her "beary" best friend. Caption, stamped in silver foil, says, "Special friends bring special joys to Christmas. 1985."

Acrylic, 3" wide
575QX372-5, $5.75 ☐

Friendship: Embroidered, Bezeled Satin; From Our House to Yours, Teacher

With Appreciation, Special Friends

New Home
Lovely Victorian homes, decorated with wreaths and Christmas greenery, encircle a blue teardrop ball. Caption: "New Home, new joys, new memories to cherish. Christmas 1985."

Blue Glass, 3″ diam.
475QX269-5, $4.75 ☐

Baby-sitter
Each of these pandas is preparing for Christmas in his own special way. The red, white and black bears present a striking contrast against the brilliant green teardrop ball. Caption: "A Baby-sitter is a special kind of friend. Christmas 1985."

Green Glass, 3″ diam.
475QX264-2, $4.75 ☐

Good Friends
Penguins frolic in the snow, making patterns and words to commemorate the holiday season. Caption on this frosted teardrop ball reads, "Good times with good friends make life's merriest moments. Christmas 1985."

White Frosted Glass, 3″ diam.
475QX265-2, $4.75 ☐

Property Ornaments

SNOOPY® and WOODSTOCK
SNOOPY® is practicing for the holiday hockey tournament with the help of his star player, WOODSTOCK. They'll skate their way into your Christmas for many years to come.

Handcrafted, 1¾″ tall
750QX491-5, $7.50 ☐

Muffin the Angel
All dressed up as an angel, Muffin is ready for the Christmas pageant wearing a snowy white fabric outfit.

Handcrafted, 2½″ tall
575QX483-5, $5.75 ☐

Kit the Shepherd
Kit is a shepherd in the Christmas pageant, dressed in a fabric headdress.

Handcrafted, 2½″ tall
575QX484-5, $5.75 ☐

Betsey Clark
This little boy is one of Betsey Clark's most charming angels. On bended knee, he gathers a little lamb into his arms.

Hand-Painted Porcelain, 2½″ tall
850QX508-5, $8.50 ☐

New Home, Baby-sitter, Good Friends

SNOOPY® *and* WOODSTOCK, *Muffin the Angel, Kit the Shepherd, Betsey Clark*

Hugga Bunch™
These little cuties share warm hugs and Christmas fun as they make their debut in the Keepsake line. Caption: "Huggy Holidays!"

Light Blue Glass, 2⅞" diam.
500QX271-5, $5.00 ☐

FRAGGLE ROCK™ Holiday
The dog, SPROCKET™, peeks in on the holiday activities of the FRAGGLE ROCK™ gang. A new property in the Keepsake Ornament line. Caption: "Happy Holidays '85."

Light Blue Glass, 3" diam.
475QX265-5, $4.75 ☐

PEANUTS®
SNOOPY® directs a Christmas chorus starring WOODSTOCK and his friends on a teardrop-shaped ball. Caption: "Sing a song of Christmas joy! 1985."

Blue Glass, 3" diam.
475QX266-5, $4.75 ☐

Norman Rockwell
Three favorite Rockwell Santa paintings appear on this frosted white ball. The caption describes the portrayals perfectly: "...He was chubby and plump, a right jolly old elf, and I laughed when I saw him, in spite of myself...C.C. Moore. From the Norman Rockwell Collection 1985."

Frosted White Glass, 2⅞" diam.
475QX266-2, $4.75 ☐

Rainbow Brite™ and Friends
Rainbow Brite and the Sprites make their first appearance in the Keepsake line amid a rainbow of colorful stars and snowflakes. Visible inside the clear glass ball is a bright gold starburst. Caption: "1985."

Clear Glass, 2⅞" diam.
475QX268-2, $4.75 ☐

A DISNEY Christmas
It's stocking-hanging time at Mickey Mouse's house as Mickey dons a Santa suit complete with a pillow for stuffing. This ornament displays a new process that allows printing directly on the glass. Dated "1985."

Pearl Blue Glass, 3" diam.
475QX271-2, $4.75 ☐

Merry Shirt Tales™
The Shirt Tales, all bundled up for winter, go skating, skiing and sledding on a teardrop-shaped ball. Caption: "Every day's a holiday when good friends get together. Christmas 1985."

Light Blue Glass, 3" diam.
475QX267-2, $4.75 ☐

Hugga Bunch, FRAGGLE ROCK™ Holiday, PEANUTS®, Norman Rockwell

Rainbow Brite™ and Friends, A DISNEY Christmas, Merry Shirt Tales™

Traditional Ornaments

Porcelain Bird
This Tufted Titmouse looks so real you might think he flew into your home to celebrate the holidays. He's fashioned of hand-painted porcelain and perches on your tree with the help of a specially designed clip.

Hand-Painted Porcelain, 2″ tall
650QX479-5, $6.50 ☐

Sewn Photoholder
A cheery array of holiday hearts and Christmas flowers are embroidered on this red fabric photoholder. Caption: "Cherished times that mean the most are kept in memory ever close. Christmas 1985."

Embroidered Fabric, 3¼″ diam.
700QX379-5, $7.00 ☐

Candle Cameo
The warmth and cheer of Christmas are captured in this portrayal of traditional holiday symbols. Subtle shadings in the ivory design accentuate the bas-relief detailing. Gold foil-stamped caption reads, "Christmas...the season that brightens the world. 1985."

Bezeled Cameo, 3″ tall
675QX374-2, $6.75 ☐

Santa Pipe
A pipe with the look of carved antique meerschaum displays a bas-relief Santa and reindeer on their Christmas Eve ride.

Handcrafted, 4½″ tall
950QX494-2, $9.50 ☐

Old-Fashioned Wreath
An intricate etched brass wreath of Christmas toys is embedded in clear acrylic. The gold foil-stamped caption says, "Christmas 1985."

Etched Brass, Acrylic, 3¼″ diam.
750QX373-5, $7.50 ☐

Peaceful Kingdom
Etched onto an acrylic oval, the lion and lamb symbolize the words that are so much a part of the meaning of Christmas: "...and peace will reign in the kingdom...Christmas 1985." Caption is stamped in gold foil.

Acrylic, 3″ wide
575QX373-2, $5.75 ☐

Christmas Treats
In the tradition of beautiful stained glass, this ornament depicts holiday candies in bright shades of red and green. A lead frame encircles the glass design. This is a new format in the Keepsake line.

Bezeled Glass, 3¼″ tall
550QX507-5, $5.50 ☐

Porcelain Bird, Sewn Photoholder, Candle Cameo, Santa Pipe

Old-Fashioned Wreath, Peaceful Kingdom, Christmas Treats

The Spirit of Santa Claus-Special Edition
Driving a green and gold sleigh laden with a bag of toys and a Christmas tree, Santa holds the reins to a beautiful prancing reindeer. The complexity and detailing of this ornament make it a true work of art. A special wishbone-shaped hanger comes with the ornament.

Handcrafted, 4¾″ tall
2250QX498-5, $22.50 ☐

Nostalgic Sled
Reissue from 1984. (See 1984 Annual Collection.)

Handcrafted, 3½″ wide
600QX442-4, $6.00

Holiday Humor

Night Before Christmas
This favorite Christmas story is at your fingertips. When you push the button, 30 pages depicting the story flip over before your eyes. Ornament comes with special stand for off-tree display.

Panorama Ball, 3¼″ diam.
1300QX449-4, $13.00 ☐

Nativity Scene
The birds and bunnies gather 'round as a group of adorable little angels welcome the Baby. This delicately detailed design illustrates the caption: "O come, all ye faithful...Christmas 1985."

Light Blue Glass, 3″ diam.
475QX264-5, $4.75 ☐

Santa's Ski Trip
Santa waves his hat as he rides to the slopes in gondola "Snowflake Mountain No. 1985." The gondola hangs by a pully with a real string "rope."

Handcrafted, 3¾″ tall
1200QX496-2, $12.00 ☐

Mouse Wagon
Bringing a gift of his favorite cheese, a white mouse rides into the Christmas season in his little red wagon. Dated "1985," the wagon has wheels that turn and a movable handle.

Handcrafted, 2″ tall
575QX476-2, $5.75 ☐

Children in the Shoe
Inspired by the nursery rhyme, this ornament depicts an old shoe house with sparkling snow on the roof, a wreath on the door and, of course, children everywhere.

Handcrafted, 3¼″ tall
950QX490-5, $9.50 ☐

The Spirit of Santa Claus

Night Before Christmas, Nativity Scene, Santa's Ski Trip, Mouse Wagon, Children in the Shoe

Do Not Disturb Bear
His green stocking is hung with care and so is his "Do not disturb 'til Christmas" sign, as the flocked bear snoozes snugly in his log. Pillow and blanket are fabric.

Handcrafted, 3" wide
775QX481-2, $7.75 ☐

Sun and Fun Santa
Santa loves the beach but he wouldn't think of going into the water without his reindeer inner tube. His bathing cap is dated " '85."

Handcrafted, 2¾" tall
775QX492-2, $7.75 ☐

Bottlecap Fun Bunnies
Mommy bunny, wearing a real pom-pom on her hat, gives baby bunny a ride. Her sled is a metal bottle cap from the "Santa Soda, North Pole Bottling Co."

Handcrafted, 2¼" tall
775QX481-5, $7.75 ☐

Lamb in Legwarmers
Little flocked lamb is ready to exercise in green, red and white crocheted fabric legwarmers.

Handcrafted, 3" tall
700QX480-2, $7.00 ☐

Candy Apple Mouse
With his tummy filled, a little white mouse naps on a partially eaten candied red apple at the end of a "1985" stick.

Handcrafted, 3¾" tall
650QX470-5, $6.50 ☐

Skateboard Raccoon
Flocked raccoon is going for a ride on a red skateboard with green, movable wheels. The design on his skateboard proclaims his star status!

Handcrafted, 2½" tall
650QX473-2, $6.50 ☐

Stardust Angel
A darling angel brushes the excess stardust from her star and keeps it in her handy "Stardust" bag.

Handcrafted, 2" tall
575QX475-2, $5.75 ☐

Soccer Beaver
This energetic beaver, dressed in red, is ready for a holiday game of soccer.

Handcrafted, 2½" tall
650QX477-5, $6.50 ☐

Beary Smooth Ride
Like children everywhere, Teddy enjoys riding all around the neighborhood. His colorful tricycle has wheels that turn.

Handcrafted, 1¾" tall
650QX480-5, $6.50 ☐

Do Not Disturb Bear, Sun and Fun Santa, Bottlecap Fun Bunnies, Lamb in Legwarmers

Candy Apple Mouse, Skateboard Raccoon, Stardust Angel, Soccer Beaver, Beary Smooth Ride

Swinging Angel Bell
Riding on a bright red swing, a little angel is the clapper of this sparkling clear bell.
Handcrafted, Glass, 3¾″ tall
1100QX492-5, $11.00 ☐

Doggy in a Stocking
Santa delivers a puppy for Christmas and he's a stocking full of charm. This tan terrier is snuggled in a stocking of crocheted red and green yarn.
Handcrafted, 3″ tall
550QX474-2, $5.50 ☐

Engineering Mouse
A white mouse is the engineer of this bright red and green train styled to look like a windup toy.
Handcrafted, 2″ tall
550QX473-5, $5.50 ☐

Kitty Mischief
Yellow and white kitten is all tangled up with a ball of real red yarn.
Handcrafted, 2″ tall
500QX474-5, $5.00 ☐

Baker Elf
An elf puts the finishing touch of green icing on his bell-shaped cookie. Centered on the cookie, "1985" appears in red icing.
Handcrafted, 3″ tall
575QX491-2, $5.75 ☐

Ice-Skating Owl
Cute white owl, wearing a red and white hat of real yarn, seems to be a bit unsteady on his new ice skates.
Handcrafted, 2″ tall
500QX476-5, $5.00 ☐

Dapper Penguin
Sporting a red top hat, gold cane and green bow tie, this dashing penguin is ready for a holiday gala.
Handcrafted, 2¼″ tall
500QX477-2, $5.00 ☐

Trumpet Panda
This flocked panda practices his holiday music for the Christmas Day parade.
Handcrafted, 2″ tall
450QX471-2, $4.50 ☐

Merry Mouse
Wearing a hat just like Santa's, this mouse can't wait until Christmas arrives. His tail is fashioned of real leather.
Handcrafted, 2½″ tall
450QX403-2, $4.50 ☐

Snow-Pitching Snowman
Flocked white snowman wearing a red and green baseball cap is all wound up and ready to pitch his snowball.
Handcrafted, 2″ tall
450QX470-2, $4.50 ☐

Swinging Angel Bell, Doggy in a Stocking, Engineering Mouse, Kitty Mischief, Baker Elf

Ice Skating Owl, Dapper Penguin, Trumpet Panda, Merry Mouse, Snow-Pitching Snowman

Three Kittens in a Mitten
Reissue from 1984. (See 1984 Annual Collection.)

Handcrafted, 3½" tall
800QX431-1, $8.00

Roller Skating Rabbit
Reissue from 1984. (See 1984 Annual Collection.)

Handcrafted, 2½" wide
500QX457-1, $5.00

Snowy Seal
Reissue from 1984. (See 1984 Annual Collection.)

Handcrafted, 1½" wide
400QX450-1, $4.00

Country Christmas Collection

Old-Fashioned Doll
She's a real Colonial lady, dressed in a holiday costume trimmed with lace. The doll has hand-painted porcelain arms, legs and head.

Hand-Painted Porcelain, Fabric, 5½" tall
1450QX519-5, $14.50 ☐

Country Goose
This delicate print on natural wood brings back memories of a simpler time. Caption: "This original design, styled in the American Country Tradition, has been printed on hardwood."

Wood, 3" diam.
775QX518-5, $7.75 ☐

Rocking Horse Memories
Silk-screen applique rocking horse is a lovely contrast against a holly-patterned background framed in an authentic wooden embroidery hoop. Caption: "Christmas 1985."

Wood, Fabric, 3¼" diam.
1000QX518-2, $10.00 ☐

Whirligig Santa
A real wood Whirligig Santa with arms that move is modeled after a popular Colonial toy.

Wood, 4" tall
1250QX519-2, $12.50 ☐

Sheep at Christmas
Reminiscent of olden-day carvings, this sheep wears a bell that rings in the holidays. Caption: "Season's Greetings 1985."

Handcrafted, 3¼" tall
825QX517-5, $8.25 ☐

Old Fashioned Doll, Country Goose, Rocking Horse Memories, Whirligig Santa, Sheep at Christmas

Keepsake Basket, Victorian Lady, Charming Angel, Lacy Heart, Snowflake

Heirloom Christmas Collection

Keepsake Basket
Hand-crocheted basket is trimmed with satin and lace. A pearl-like button closure opens to a rose-scented sachet.

Fabric, 2½" tall
1500QX514-5, $15.00 ☐

Victorian Lady
Hand-painted porcelain doll rests on a burgundy satin, lace-trimmed cone.

Hand-Painted Porcelain, Fabric, 3¾" tall
950QX513-2, $9.50 ☐

Charming Angel
A precious angel with yarn hair and wings of sheer netting wears a hand-sewn lace dress and holds a satin rose.

Fabric, 3¾" tall
975QX512-5, $9.75 ☐

Lacy Heart
A romantic padded satin heart is lavishly trimmed with lace and scented with a rose sachet.

Fabric, 3" tall
875QX511-2, $8.75 ☐

Snowflake
This hand-crocheted snowflake is padded with burgundy satin and laced with intricate detail.

Fabric, 4¼" diam.
650QX510-5, $6.50 ☐

Limited Edition

Heavenly Trumpeter
The second limited edition ornament is a hand-painted porcelain angel, playing a golden trumpet to announce the joyous tidings of the season. The ornament, limited to an edition size of 24,700, comes with a wooden display stand.

Hand-Painted Porcelain, 5" tall
2750QX405-2, $27.50 ☐

Collectible Series

Windows of the World—First Edition
An adorable Mexican child sits in a brick and stucco window in this first of a series of worldwide celebrations of Christmas. A "1985" pinata and Christmas greeting, "Feliz Navidad," decorate the archway.

Handcrafted, 3" tall
975QX490-2, $9.75 ☐

Miniature Creche—First Edition
A series of unique Nativities fashioned in different media such as wood and porcelain.

1985 875QX482-5 Wood and Straw ☐

Heavenly Trumpeter

Windows of the World, Miniature Creche

Nostalgic Houses and Shops—Second Edition
The town is growing with the addition of this second ornament, an "Old-Fashioned Toy Shop." A counter, cash register, dollhouse and toy truck identify the toy store downstairs, but the owner lives on the fully furnished second floor. The address on the door is "1985."

Handcrafted, 2½″ tall
1375QX497-5, $13.75 ☐

Art Masterpiece—Second Edition
The famous *Madonna of the Pomegranate* is reproduced on padded satin. Caption: "Madonna of the Pomegranate (ca. 1487), The Uffizi Gallery, Florence, Italy."

Bezeled Satin, 2¾″ diam.
675QX377-2, $6.75 ☐

Wood Childhood Ornaments—Second Edition
The second in this nostalgic series is a hand-painted "Wooden Train" and log car. Loaded with logs for holiday fireplaces, the train has wheels that turn and a real pull string.

Hand-Painted Wood, 3½″ wide
700QX472-2, $7.00 ☐

Twelve Days of Christmas—Second Edition
Two turtle doves etched on an acrylic heart represent the second day of the popular Christmas carol. Gold foil-stamped caption reads, "The Twelve Days of Christmas 1985. Two turtle doves..."

Acrylic, 3″ tall
650QX371-2, $6.50 ☐

Porcelain Bear—Third Edition
The third "Cinnamon Bear" is enjoying his big peppermint candy cane. Every detail is hand painted, including the tiny button on his middle!

Hand-Painted Porcelain, 2¼″ tall
750QX479-2, $7.50 ☐

Tin Locomotive—Fourth Edition
This pressed tin locomotive has wheels that turn and a bell that jingles. Precisely detailed, the ornament is fashioned after an antique train and carries the date "1985."

Pressed Tin, 3½″ tall
1475QX497-2, $14.75 ☐

Holiday Wildlife—Fourth Edition
Two beautiful partridge stand in a field of colorful foliage. The natural wood frame complements the winter scene. Caption: "California Partridge, Lophortyx Californica, Fourth in a Series, Wildlife Collection, Christmas 1985."

Wood, 3″ diam.
750QX376-5, $7.50 ☐

Nostalgic Houses and Shops, Art Masterpiece, Wood Childhood Ornaments, Twelve Days of Christmas

Porcelain Bear, Tin Locomotive, Holiday Wildlife

Clothespin Soldier—Fourth Edition
The "Scottish Highlander" is dressed in his clan's colorful fabric kilt and has a real pom-pom on his red tam. His arms are movable.

Handcrafted, 2½" tall
550QX471-5, $5.50 ☐

Rocking Horse—Fifth Edition
A brown and white pinto pony rides the range on blue rockers dated "1985." His saddle and trappings are green and red and his flying yarn tail is brown.

Handcrafted, 4" wide
1075QX493-2, $10.75 ☐

Norman Rockwell—Sixth Edition
The "Jolly Postman" is making his daily deliveries accompanied by the neighborhood kids who can't wait to see what he's bringing. The white bas-relief design appears against a pale green background. Caption stamped in silver foil reads, "Jolly Postman, Sixth in a Series, Christmas 1985, The Norman Rockwell Collection."

Cameo, 3" diam.
750QX374-5, $7.50 ☐

Here Comes Santa-Seventh Edition
"Santa's Fire Engine" from the "North Pole Fire Department" is the seventh in this series. Wearing fire hat number "85," Santa rides this old-fashioned red and gold fire engine.

Handcrafted, 3" tall
1400QX496-5, $14.00 ☐

Frosty Friends—Sixth Edition
These two Arctic pals row a red "1985" kayak into a new holiday season while enjoying their position as number six in the series.

Handcrafted, 2" tall
850QX482-2, $8.50 ☐

Betsey Clark—Thirteenth and Final Edition
In their final appearance on a series ball ornament, artist Betsey Clark's angelic children are busy playing and dreaming among the clouds and keeping the stars shiny for Christmas. Caption: "Christmas brings a special kind of feeling. 1985."

White Glass, 3¼" diam.
500QX263-2, $5.00 ☐

Thimble—Eighth Edition
"Thimble Santa" carries a Christmas tree in his handy thimble backpack. The "rope" holding the thimble is made of real string.

Handcrafted, 2⅜" tall
550QX472-5, $5.50 ☐

Clothespin Soldier, Rocking Horse, Norman Rockwell

Here Comes Santa, Frosty Friends, Betsey Clark, Thimble

THE 1986 COLLECTION

The year 1986 may become known as the "magical" year for ornament collectors because of the popularity of the limited edition "Magical Unicorn." Four months after it was offered, it became virtually impossible to find, and was the most searched-for ornament of the year.

Another 1986 ornament also appeared at the top of the collectors' "must-have" list. It commemorates the birthday of the most beloved "Lady" of the land and was, of course, the acrylic "Statue of Liberty."

Three Collectible Series debuted in 1986. The new ball series, "Betsey Clark: Home for Christmas," follows one year after the first Betsey Clark ball series ended. Santa's better half co-stars in the second new 1986 series, "Mr. and Mrs. Claus." And the third new series, "Reindeer Champs," transforms Santa's reindeer into comtemporary athletes. One series, "Art Masterpiece," came to an end with a third classic work of art.

New formats in '86 jingle, squeak, and tap-tap-tap! The "L'il Jingler" ornament features a handcrafted raccoon hanging onto a chain dotted with jingle bells. The chain was designed to dangle between two branches of the tree. The "Chatty Penguin" plush ornament makes a squeaking noise, and the handcrafted "Little Drummers" actually tap their tiny drums.

"Heathcliff" and "Paddington™ Bear" make their premiere appearance as do ornaments for "Husband," "Nephew" and "Sweetheart." Collectors of country items were happy to see the "American Country" collection of four coordinated glass balls by Mary Emmerling, and the "Country Treasures" collection of handcrafted and porcelain ornaments. In addition, the "Christmas Medley" collection features designs centering on a musical theme.

Commemoratives

Baby's First Christmas

Painted in soft pastels, this realistic miniature mobile has four of Baby's favorite things. A toy duck, Santa, teddy bear, and stocking dangle from an acrylic cloud topped with a star bearing the caption, "Baby's First Christmas 1986."

Handcrafted, 3½ " tall
900QX412-6, $9.00 ☐

Baby's First Christmas Photoholder

As sweet as Baby's picture, this heart-shaped gingham photoholder is decorated with white lace and delicate embroidery. Front Caption: "Baby's First Christmas." Back Caption: "A Baby puts special magic in holiday moments. 1986."

Fabric, 3¾ " tall
800QX379-2, $8.00 ☐

Baby's First Christmas

An acrylic lamb, with an etched coat that looks like curly wool, brings Baby a holiday stocking captioned, "1986 Baby's First Christmas," stamped in gold foil.

Acrylic, 3¾ " tall
600QX380-3, $6.00 ☐

Baby's First Christmas: Handcrafted, Photoholder, Acrylic

Baby's First Christmas

Baby loves to ride his rocking horse and so does Teddy Bear on this ecru satin ball topped with a handcrafted bear. The rockers carry the caption, "Baby's First Christmas 1986." The message, "A Baby's a bundle of hope and joy," appears on a bright red heart.

Ecru Satin, 2⅞" diam.
550QX271-3, $5.50 ☐

Grandchild's First Christmas

A beary sleepy flocked bear dreams of Christmas on a lace-trimmed fabric pillow nestled in a straw basket. "Grandchild's First Christmas 1986" appears on the tag.

Handcrafted, 2¼" tall
1000QX411-6, $10.00 ☐

Baby's Second Christmas

His diaper is slipping, but that won't stop this adorable mouse from delivering a little toy mouse snuggled inside a stocking. Caption: "Baby's 2nd Christmas 1986."

Handcrafted, 1¾" tall
650QX413-3, $6.50 ☐

Child's Third Christmas

Dressed in soft fabric sleepers and cap, this flocked panda is trying to wait up for Santa. His bib reads, "My Third Christmas 1986."

Fabric, 2 11/32" tall
650QX413-6, $6.50 ☐

Baby Locket

Embossed lettering and baby toys decorate this textured brass locket. Inside is space for Baby's photograph and for personalization. "Baby" appears on the front and "1986" on the back. The ornament may be displayed open or closed and comes with a wishbone hanger.

Textured Brass, 2¼" diam.
1600QX412-3, $16.00 ☐

Husband

The "Husband" ornament is a new caption in the Keepsake line. Accented with touches of color, the intricately detailed, bas-relief duck decoy design is a traditional favorite. The sentiment on the reverse reads, "A Husband is a forever friend. Christmas 1986."

Cameo, 2¾" diam.
800QX383-6, $8.00 ☐

Sister

Printed on red padded satin, the cuddly teddy bear sitting inside a country grapevine wreath eagerly awaits Christmas. The ornament is framed in brass and carries the caption, "With every Christmas, every year, a Sister grows more loved...more dear. 1986."

Bezeled Satin, 2¾" diam.
675QX380-6, $6.75 ☐

Baby's First Christmas: Satin Ball; Grandchild's First Christmas

Baby's Second Christmas, Child's Third Christmas, Baby Locket

Husband, Sister

Mother and Dad, Mother, Father

Daughter, Son

Niece, Nephew

Grandmother, Grandparents

Mother and Dad
Vivid holiday candles, symbolizing the warmth a family shares, decorate a snowy white porcelain bell tied with a red ribbon. Caption: "For a Mother and Dad who are warmly loved. Christmas 1986."

Fine Porcelain, 5½" tall
750QX431-6, $7.50 ☐

Mother
The etched and frosted background of this bezeled acrylic ornament provides an attractive contrast to the clear heart in the center. The heart holds the caption stamped in gold foil, "A Mother's love reflects the warmth of Christmas all year through. 1986."

Acrylic, 2¾" diam.
700QX382-6, $7.00 ☐

Father
A festive French horn, printed in silver, decorates the front of this wooden ornament for Father. On the reverse the caption reads, "Nothing can ever replace the wisdom, guidance and love of a Father. Christmas 1986."

Wood, 3¼" diam.
650QX431-3, $6.50 ☐

Daughter
Fashioned to look like wood, the little girl in this knit stocking captures the nostalgia of an Old-World European toy. Caption: "For Daughter 1986."

Handcrafted, 3½" tall
575QX430-6, $5.75 ☐

Son
Similar to the girl in the "Daughter" ornament, the little boy in this knitted stocking is designed to look like a wooden European toy of years past. Caption: "For Son 1986."

Handcrafted, 4" tall
575QX430-3, $5.75 ☐

Niece
The white cat and interesting shapes and patterns in this silk-screened design give the ornament a fresh, contemporary look. A red feather-edge satin ribbon circles the wood embroidery hoop. Caption: "Nieces give the nicest gifts...beauty, joy and love. Christmas 1986."

Fabric and Wood, 4½" tall
600QX426-6, $6.00 ☐

Nephew
A crisp white snowman, accented with bright touches of red, stands out vividly against a dark blue sky in this graphic design. Bezeled in chrome, this lacquer-look ornament carries the sentiment, "To wish a special Nephew a happy holiday season! 1986."

Bezeled Lacquer-Look, 2¾" diam.
675QX381-3, $6.25 ☐

Granddaughter, Grandson, Godchild

Grandmother
A country quilt design of Christmas trees decorates the center of an ivory satin ball capped with a golden crown. "A Grandmother's love is for always" and "Christmas 1986" appear on two of the trees located on opposite sides of the ball.

Ivory Satin, 2⅞" diam.
475QX274-3, $4.75 ☐

Grandparents
A stitchery design in holiday green and red accented with gold decorates a white porcelain bell for Grandparents. Two colorful doves appear on the front with the words, "Christmas 1986." The sentiment on the back reads, "Grandparents are never far from thought...ever near in love."

Fine Porcelain, 5½" tall
750QX432-3, $7.50 ☐

Granddaughter
Antique scenes of children enjoying the holiday are accented with gold on a frosted glass ball fashioned to appeal to Granddaughters of all ages. Caption: "Season after season, a Granddaughter grows dearer and dearer. Christmas 1986."

White Glass, 2⅞" diam.
475QX273-6, $4.75 ☐

Grandson
A sign in the forest proclaims it's "Christmas 1986." As a jolly beaver brings a tree home for the animals on this teardrop ball, a bunny carries a banner that says, "A Grandson is a bringer of a very special kind of love."

Blue Glass, 3" diam.
475QX273-3, $4.75 ☐

Godchild
Brightly dressed appliqued teddy bears circle a white satin ball capped with a golden crown. Two bears hold a banner that reads, "Christmas 1986." Caption: "A Godchild is a very special someone."

White Satin, 2⅞" diam.
475QX271-6, $4.75 ☐

First Christmas Together
This romantic brass locket holds two of your favorite photographs. The embossed caption, "First Christmas Together 1986," decorates the front, and embossed ribbon and doves appear on the back. The locket comes with a wishbone hanger.

Textured Brass, 2¼" tall
1600QX400-3, $16.00 ☐

First Christmas Together
Two turtledoves, timeless symbols of love, appear in a miniature birdcage captioned "First Christmas Together 1986." The water and seed dishes are frosted acrylic, and the bars are polished brass.

Handcrafted, 4" tall
1200QX409-6, $12.00 ☐

First Christmas Together
A contemporary design of etched entwined hearts marks a very special Christmas. The acrylic teardrop, framed in chrome, carries the silver foil caption, "First Christmas Together 1986."

Acrylic, 3$^{11}/_{32}$" tall
7000QX379-3, $7.00 ☐

First Christmas Together
The artist used a torn-paper design technique to create the wintry landscape on this light green glass ball. Two redbirds appear next to the words, "First Christmas Together 1986." On the other side is the sentiment, "How beautiful the season when it's filled with love."

Light Green Glass, 2⅞" diam.
475QX270-3, $4.75 ☐

Ten Years Together
Accented with gold, the roses and holly on this porcelain bell look like cloisonne. Front Caption: "Ten Years Together Christmas 1986." Back Caption: "More than yesterday...less than tomorrow."

Fine Porcelain, 3" tall
750QX401-3, $7.50 ☐

Twenty-Five Years Together
Made of fine porcelain, this miniature collector's plate ornament commemorates an enduring love. The front of the plate features blue holiday bells accented with silver. Front Caption: "Twenty-Five Years Together Christmas 1986." Back Caption: "Love lights all the seasons of our years." Plate stand included.

Fine Porcelain, 3¼" diam.
800QX410-3, $8.00 ☐

Fifty Years Together
Made of snowy white bisque porcelain, this bell is adorned with a glazed bas-relief holly design. Caption: "Fifty Years Together" and "Christmas 1986." The glazed porcelain handle is a sculpted number "50."

Fine Porcelain, 3$^{13}/_{32}$" tall
1000QX400-6, $10.00 ☐

First Christmas Together: Textured Brass, Handcrafted, Acrylic, Green Glass

Ten Years Together, Twenty-Five Years Together, Fifty Years Together

Loving Memories
This miniature heart-shaped shadow box has the look of wood. It holds a brass bell, teddy bear and Christmas gift, and has room for a tiny memento of your own. The tag on the package carries the date "1986."

Handcrafted, 5¼" tall
900QX409-3, $9.00 ☐

Timeless Love
A sprig of mistletoe, delicately etched at the top of this heart-shaped acrylic ornament, accents the gold foil-stamped sentiment, "Love...comes not in moments in time, but in timeless moments. Christmas 1986."

Acrylic, 3" tall
600QX379-6, $6.00 ☐

Sweetheart
This ornament is a new caption in the Keepsake line. The exquisitely detailed gazebo holds a miniature bottle-brush tree decorated with tiny beaded garland. Two signs read, "To My Sweetheart With Love" and "Christmas 1986." The bottom of the ornament has space for personalization.

Handcrafted, 3½" tall
1100QX408-6, $11.00 ☐

Season of the Heart
An old-fashioned sleigh ride evokes the warm spirit of the season and the love a family shares. Caption: "Christmas... season of the heart, time of fond remembrance."

Red Glass, 2⅞" diam.
475QX270-6, $4.75 ☐

Friendship Greeting
Contrasting silk-screened fabric patterns were used to create this cheery envelope ornament. The red fabric with a holly and dot pattern reverses inside to ivory fabric with a tiny red and green pattern. The enclosed card carries the message, "Friends are forever," and provides space for personalization. Caption on back of envelope reads, "Merry Christmas 1986."

Fabric, 2¾" tall
800QX427-3, $8.00 ☐

Joy of Friends
The ice-skating scene, reproduced from stitchery and printed on padded satin, captures the look of American folk art. Framed in chrome, the horizontal oval carries the words, "Friends make the heart warmer, the day merrier, the season more memorable."

Bezeled Satin, 2¾" tall
675QX382-3, $6.75 ☐

Loving Memories, Timeless Love

Sweetheart, Season of the Heart

Friendship Greeting, Joy of Friends

Friendship's Gift
Fashioned in the shape of a traditional Christmas ornament, this acrylic keepsake carries a message of friendship and an adorable etched mouse playing Santa's helper. The caption is stamped in gold foil: "Friendship is a gift. Christmas 1986."

Acrylic, 3" tall
600QX381-6, $6.00 ☐

From Our Home to Yours
Etched onto a teardrop-shaped acrylic ornament is a finely detailed straw basket of fruit—a warm symbol of friendship and welcome. The caption, "From Our Home to Yours Christmas 1986," is stamped in silver foil.

Acrylic, 3¼" tall
600QX383-3, $6.00 ☐

Gratitude
Inside a wooden embroidery hoop, a vivid cardinal and holly design is silk-screened onto white satin. The caption, "Especially to thank you...especially at Christmas 1986," is printed in a matching shade of green.

Satin and Wood, 5" tall
600QX432-6, $6.00 ☐

Friends Are Fun
The design on this light blue glass ball is similar to designs in the "Frosty Friends" Collectible Series. A playful pair of Arctic pals riding a sleigh pulled by a team of Husky puppies illustrates the sentiment, "It's fun having friends to go 'round with. Christmas 1986."

Light Blue Glass, 2⅞" diam.
475QX272-3, $4.75 ☐

New Home
A yummy neighborhood of cookie homes and gingerbread people decorates a white frosted teardrop ball. Designed to look like icing, the caption reads, "Christmas is so special when it's spent in a new home." One of the houses carries the address "1986."

White Glass, 3" diam.
475QX274-6, $4.75 ☐

Teacher
A little mouse has nibbled a star in his apple for the teacher. An apple on the other side of the white glass ball carries the caption, "For My Teacher Christmas 1986."

White Glass, 2⅞" diam.
475QX275-3, $4.75 ☐

Friendship's Gift, From Our Home To Yours, Gratitude

Friends Are Fun, New Home, Teacher

Baby-Sitter

The word "baby-sitter" is absent from the sentiment on this gold teardrop ball to make the ornament suitable for the many different people who take care of children. The design of colorful antique toys evokes memories of childhood. Caption on the Toy Top: "For being the best friend a child could ever have." On the Horse: "Christmas 1986."

Gold Glass, 3" diam.
475QX275-6, $4.75 ☐

Property Ornaments

The Statue of Liberty

A beautifully etched likeness adorns this acrylic ornament created in honor of the statue's 100th birthday. The gold foil-stamped caption reads, "The Lady 1886 Centennial 1986."

Acrylic, $3\frac{9}{16}$" tall
600QX384-3, $6.00 ☐

SNOOPY® and WOODSTOCK

SNOOPY® and his favorite pal WOODSTOCK enjoy a ride on their new saucer-shaped sled called the "Beagle Express."

Handcrafted, $1\frac{3}{4}$" tall
800QX434-6, $8.00 ☐

Heathcliff

The little angel watching over Heathcliff reminds this sassy cat to be good. His behavior has been perfect, or so he says in his letter: "Dear Santa, I've been exceptional. Heathcliff."

Handcrafted, $3\frac{3}{32}$" tall
750QX436-3, $7.50 ☐

Katybeth

Pretty Katybeth is an angel who makes friends with everyone, including a smiling star that passes her way. The ornament is made of fine porcelain and has been painted by hand in pastels.

Hand-Painted Fine Porcelain, $2\frac{19}{32}$" tall
700QX435-3, $7.00 ☐

Paddington™ Bear

A favorite of both young and old, Paddington™ Bear can't imagine a nicer Christmas gift than a fresh jar of honey. His hat carries his name, "Paddington," and his jar is decorated with a red fabric bow.

Handcrafted, $2\frac{9}{16}$" tall
600QX435-6, $6.00 ☐

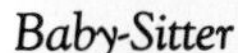
Baby-Sitter

The Statue of Liberty

SNOOPY® and WOODSTOCK, Heathcliff, Katybeth, Paddington™ Bear

Norman Rockwell
The three "Christmas Scenes" on this summer green ball are owned exclusively by Hallmark. Both the sentiment and the paintings reflect the excitement of the holiday season. Caption: "Christmas time is filled with joy and glad anticipation, and all the loving reasons for a happy celebration."

Green Glass, 2⅞" diam.
475QX276-3, $4.75 ☐

PEANUTS®
WOODSTOCK and his friends go ice skating with SNOOPY® on a sky blue glass teardrop ball. They perform pirouettes and etch "Merry Christmas" into the smooth surface. A sign announces it's "1986."

Blue Glass, 3" diam.
475QX276-6, $4.75 ☐

Shirt Tales™ Parade
The Shirt Tales™ make beautiful music as they parade around a gold glass ball. The drum major's shirt reads, "Here Comes Christmas!" and the ornament is captioned, "Merriment is all around whenever Christmas comes to town!"

Gold Glass, 2⅞" diam.
475QX277-3, $4.75 ☐

Norman Rockwell, PEANUTS®, Shirt Tales™ Parade

Holiday Humor

Santa's Hot Tub
Santa and his reindeer pal know there's no better way to recover from that long Christmas Eve journey than to spend a leisurely hour in the hot tub. The tub looks like wood, and the shower pipes are made of brass wire. Caption: "Polar Barrel Hot Tub Co."

Handcrafted, 3" tall
1200QX426-3, $12.00 ☐

Playful Possum
A handcrafted opossum is the clapper inside a clear glass holiday bell. He's in his favorite position—upside down— and holds a translucent lollipop decorated with a Christmas tree.

Handcrafted, Glass, 3 23/32" tall
1100QX425-3, $11.00 ☐

Treetop Trio
A trio of bluebirds chirps a carol for Christmas in a cozy nest made of real straw. The ornament attaches to your tree with a special clip.

Handcrafted, 2" tall
1100QX425-6, $11.00 ☐

Wynken, Blynken and Nod
A beloved nursery rhyme comes to life. Pearly blue waves lap at the boat draped with silver nets. The names, "Wynken, Blynken, and Nod," appear on the stern.

Handcrafted, 2⅞" tall
975QX424-6, $9.75 ☐

Santa's Hot Tub, Playful Possum, Treetop Trio, Wynken, Blynken and Nod

Acorn Inn
Mr. Squirrel announces the opening of the holiday season at the snowcapped "Acorn Inn" by displaying a festive Christmas wreath.

Handcrafted, 2" tall
850QX424-3, $8.50 □

Touchdown Santa
Santa is the hero of the game, heading for the end zone to score a touchdown. His name, "S. Claus," is printed on the back of his red jersey and his number, "86," appears on front and back.

Handcrafted, $2\frac{15}{16}$" tall
800QX423-3, $8.00 □

Snow Buddies
The little mouse gets a big hug from the flocked snowmouse he has built for Christmas. The snowmouse's arms were molded from real sticks, and he wears a soft fabric muffler. His pal has a leather tail.

Handcrafted, $2\frac{1}{4}$" tall
800QX423-6, $8.00 □

Open Me First
The box is labeled, "Open Me First 1986," and that's just what the child does on Christmas morning. He finds what he always wanted inside—a kitten. The tissue inside the box is painted a pearly white, and the ornament attaches to your tree with a clip.

Handcrafted, $2\frac{15}{16}$" tall
725QX422-6, $7.25 □

Rah Rah Rabbit
Waving a real pompom, the holiday's cheeriest cheerleader inspires her team to victory. Her sweater carries the name of her school, "North Pole High," and her megaphone displays the number "86."

Handcrafted, $2\frac{1}{2}$" tall
700QX421-6, $7.00 □

Tipping the Scales
Santa's weight of "198.6" on the scale shows that his belly still shakes "like a bowl full of jelly." But he's really just fashionably plump wearing a robe monogrammed with an "S" and holding his favorite snack—a chocolate chip cookie.

Handcrafted, $2\frac{11}{16}$" tall
675QX418-6, $6.75 □

Li'l Jingler
A chain dotted with brass jingle bells has a hook at each end to let this playful raccoon dangle between two branches of your tree. He wears a sporty fabric bow tie.

Handcrafted, 2" tall
675QX419-3, $6.75 □

Ski Tripper
Wearing a flocked red jumpsuit, this little skier spends her holidays on the slopes.

Handcrafted, $2\frac{1}{8}$" tall
675QX420-6, $6.75 □

Acorn Inn, Touchdown Santa, Snow Buddies

Open Me First, Rah Rah Rabbit, Tipping the Scales

Li'l Jingler, Ski Tripper

Popcorn Mouse
This ornament displays charming touches of authenticity. Real cranberries and popcorn were used to mold the design, and the mouse strings his garland with a metal needle. He has a white leather tail and sits on a spool of red yarn labeled, "Chris-Mouse Sewing Co. Est. 1986."

Handcrafted, 2½" tall
675QX421-3, $6.75 ☐

Puppy's Best Friend
Man's best friend has his own best friend—a little elf who brings him a Christmas bone.

Handcrafted, 2¼" tall
650QX420-3, $6.50 ☐

Happy Christmas to Owl
Sitting on his perch, an owl reads a classic story to his little friend. The story is familiar with some small variations: "I heard him exclaim, ere he drove out of sight, Happy Christmas to owl, and to owl a good-nite." The book's title is "Christmas Stories."

Handcrafted, 3" tall
600QX418-3, $6.00 ☐

Walnut Shell Rider
Comfortably seated in his walnut shell sled, a merry old elf holds on to the cord ropes for a smooth downhill ride. A real walnut was used to mold this design.

Handcrafted, 1¾" tall
600QX419-6, $6.00 ☐

Heavenly Dreamer
This little angel, wearing a brass wire halo, takes a short nap on a frosted acrylic cloud. Stars and holly decorate her billowy bed.

Handcrafted, 1⅜" tall
575QX417-3, $5.75 ☐

Mouse in the Moon
Dressed for the holiday season, this playful mouse likes what he sees — his own reflection in the mirrored moon. His little leather tail peeps out of his sleepers.

Handcrafted, 2¾" tall
550QX416-6, $5.50 ☐

Merry Koala
When he tried on Santa's knitted red cap, this soft flocked koala discovered that Santa's a big guy!

Handcrafted, 2" tall
500QX415-3, $5.00 ☐

Chatty Penguin
He's chubby and soft and he speaks! When you shake this plush penguin he makes a squeaking noise. The format is new to the Keepsake line.

Plush, 3⅝" tall
575QX417-6, $5.75 ☐

Popcorn Mouse, Puppy's Best Friend, Happy Christmas to Owl, Walnut Shell Rider

Heavenly Dreamer, Mouse in the Moon, Merry Koala, Chatty Penguin

Special Delivery
Tucked under the penguin's wing is a gift can of "Sardines" for a lucky friend. The can is topped with a red fabric bow.

Handcrafted, 2" tall
500QX415-6, $5.00 ☐

Jolly Hiker
Wearing a backpack and a bedroll, Santa hikes up the hill using his candy cane walking stick. There are just some places a sleigh and eight reindeer can't go!

Handcrafted, 2" tall
500QX483-2, $5.00 ☐

Cookies for Santa
If Santa gets hungry on Christmas Eve, he'll enjoy this plate of cookies. The sign says they're "For Santa," and the frosted star cookie is dated "1986."

Handcrafted, 2¾" diam.
450QX414-6, $4.50 ☐

Merry Mouse
Reissue from 1985. (See 1985 Annual Collection.)

Handcrafted, 2½" tall
450QX403-2, $4.50 ☐

Skateboard Raccoon
Reissue from 1985. (See 1985 Annual Collection.)

Handcrafted, 2½" tall
650QX473-2, $6.50 ☐

Beary Smooth Ride
Reissue from 1985. (See 1985 Annual Collection.)

Handcrafted, 1¾" tall
650QX480-5, $6.50 ☐

Snow-Pitching Snowman
Reissue from 1985. (See 1985 Annual Collection.)

Handcrafted, 2" tall
450QX470-2, $4.50 ☐

Kitty Mischief
Reissue from 1985. (See 1985 Annual Collection.)

Handcrafted, 2" tall
500QX474-5, $5.00 ☐

Special Edition

Jolly St. Nick
In the 1800s, cartoonist Thomas Nast introduced a new style of St. Nicholas to the world—the modernized, grandfatherly Santa we all love today. This Special Edition ornament captures Nast's vision of the "jolly old elf" in fine porcelain that has been carefully painted by hand.

Hand-Painted Fine Porcelain, 5½" tall
2250QX429-6, $22.50 ☐

Special Delivery, Jolly Hiker, Cookies for Santa

Soccer Beaver
Reissue from 1985. (See 1985 Annual Collection.)

Handcrafted, 2½" tall
650QX477-5, $6.50 ☐

Do Not Disturb Bear
Reissue from 1985. (See 1985 Annual Collection.)

Handcrafted, 3" wide.
775QX481-2, $7.75 ☐

Jolly St. Nick

Limited Edition

Magical Unicorn

This fine porcelain unicorn may, indeed, be magical because it has become one of the most sought after ornaments in the history of the Keepsake line. Hand-painted pastel flowers circle the unicorn's neck and are woven through his mane. Matching green and pink fabric ribbons are draped around his body, and his hooves and horn are painted silver. Limited to an edition size of 24,700 pieces, the ornament comes with a wooden display stand.

Hand-Painted Fine Porcelain, 4½" tall
2750QX429-3, $27.50 ☐

Christmas Medley Collection

Joyful Carolers

This design, sculpted to look like hand-carved wood, is reminiscent of the "Nostalgia" ornaments from years past. Dressed in the style of Dickens' characters, the carolers are fully dimensional. Caption on front and back: "Joy to the World 1986."

Handcrafted, 3¼" diam.
975QX513-6, $9.75 ☐

Festive Treble Clef

Let the music begin! A tiny brass bell dangles from a shiny treble clef, accented with translucent red and tied with a striped fabric ribbon.

Handcrafted, 3⅞" tall
875QX513-3, $8.75 ☐

Favorite Tin Drum

The tin drum, a favorite of children for generations, is reproduced in miniature including two tiny drumsticks. A delicate holly design decorates both drumheads, and the bindings are made of gold cord.

Tin, 2" diam.
850QX514-3, $8.50 ☐

Christmas Guitar

Decorated front and back with a green and red holly design, this miniature guitar is dated "1986" and hangs from its own guitar strap made of striped fabric ribbon. The tiny frets are accented with gold.

Handcrafted, 3" tall
700QX512-6, $7.00 ☐

Holiday Horn

Made of velvety bisque porcelain, this graceful horn is accented with touches of gold and tied with a striped fabric ribbon. The holly design seen on the "Favorite Tin Drum" adorns the ivory surface outside the horn's mouth.

Fine Porcelain, 3" tall
800QX514-6, $8.00 ☐

Magical Unicorn

Country Treasures Collection

All of the ornaments in this collection are packaged in a wooden Shaker box.

Country Sleigh

Modeled after an antique sleigh, this ornament evokes memories of an old-fashioned Christmas. Dated "1986," the sleigh holds a plaid fabric blanket—just the right thing for a crisp country morning!

Handcrafted, 2" tall
1000QX511-3, $10.00 ☐

Remembering Christmas

The vivid country quilt pattern re-created on this fine porcelain ornament will appeal to both plate and ornament collectors. Dated "1986," the back of the miniature plate displays the sentiment, "Christmas memories are keepsakes of the heart." Plate stand included.

Fine Porcelain, 3¼" diam.
875QX510-6, $8.75 ☐

Little Drummers

Motion is the special feature of this unique ornament. The three little drummer boys, fashioned to look like wood, actually play their drums when you tap or shake the ornament's platform. A novel variation on a favorite symbol of the season.

Handcrafted, 4" tall
1250QX511-6, $12.50 ☐

Nutcracker Santa

This Santa's not a real nutcracker, of course, but he's crafted to look like one. When you lift the tassel on his cap, his mouth pops open. Carefully painted and antiqued, the design resembles hand-carved wood.

Handcrafted, 3⅜" tall
1000QX512-3, $10.00 ☐

Welcome, Christmas

Dangling inside a heart-shaped frame, a little angel brings a warm country welcome. The frame, decorated with a delicate stencil-look design of hearts and greenery, carries the caption, "Welcome, Christmas! 1986."

Handcrafted, 2⅝" tall
825QX510-3, $8.25 ☐

Joyful Carolers, Festive Treble Clef

Favorite Tin Drum, Christmas Guitar, Holiday Horn

Country Sleigh, Remembering Christmas

Little Drummers, Nutcracker Santa, Welcome, Christmas

Traditional Ornaments

Holiday Jingle Bell
Crafted in the shape of a jingle bell, this French blue and white musical ornament plays a very appropriate melody: "Jingle Bells." Eight tiny bas-relief reindeer race gracefully around a band in the center. Caption: "Merry Christmas 1986."

Handcrafted, 2¾″ diam.
1600QX404-6, $16.00 ☐

Memories to Cherish
A braided ceramic wreath, with brightly painted bow and holly, is a photoholder for the holiday tree. Caption: "A memory to cherish. Christmas 1986."

Ceramic, 3⅛″ tall
750QX427-6, $7.50 ☐

Bluebird
This red-breasted bluebird, a symbol of happiness, appears to have just landed on a Christmas tree branch. He's made of hand-painted fine porcelain and attaches with a special clip.

Hand-Painted Fine Porcelain, $3\frac{5}{16}$″ tall
725QX428-3, $7.25 ☐

Glowing Christmas Tree
A lacy brass Christmas tree, trimmed with colorful stars, is embedded in a teardrop acrylic ornament. The date, "1986," appears on the tree's base.

Embedded Acrylic, 3¼″ diam.
700QX428-6, $7.00 ☐

Heirloom Snowflake
Delicate hand-crocheted trim decorates padded lavender-blue satin to create this lacy snowflake.

Fabric, 4¾″ tall
675QX515-3, $6.75 ☐

Christmas Beauty
Inspired by the sensitive and subtle designs of the Orient, this lacquer-look ornament reflects the spirit of the season. Caption: "Christmas comes gently, touching the world with beauty, filling it with joy."

Lacquer-Look, 2¾″ diam.
600QX322-3, $6.00 ☐

Star Brighteners
Two charming etched angels polish a star for Christmas. The gold foil-stamped caption, "Joy at Christmas 1986," makes the star glow.

Acrylic, 2¾″ diam.
600QX322-6, $6.00 ☐

The Magi
On a gold glass teardrop ball, the Magi come to Christmas once more. Caption: "O come let us adore Him. Christmas 1986."

Gold Glass, 3″ diam.
475QX272-6, $4.75 ☐

Holiday Jingle Bell, Memories to Cherish, Bluebird, Glowing Chritmas Tree

Heirloom Snowflake, Christmas Beauty, Star Brighteners, The Magi

Mary Emmerling: American Country Collection

Mary Emmerling is a well-known designer and authority on country decor. Her collection of four coordinated glass balls has the speckled look of spatterware and was inspired by popular design motifs found in 19th-century American homes.

White and Blue Glass, 2⅞″ diam.
795QX275-2, $7.95 ☐

Collectible Series

Mr. and Mrs. Claus—First Edition

Mrs. Claus starts this series out with a holiday kiss for her hubby. Standing under the mistletoe she thoughtfully provides, he holds a list dated "1986." Aptly named "Merry Mistletoe Time," the ornament is first in this new series.

Handcrafted, 3 7/16″ tall
1300QX402-6, $13.00 ☐

Reindeer Champs—First Edition

"Dasher" lives up to his name as he jogs around Santa's workshop in preparation for his Christmas Eve journey. Wearing a shirt that says "Dasher 86," he's the first in this series of reindeer sports stars.

Handcrafted, 2⅞″ tall
750QX422-3, $7.50 ☐

Betsey Clark: Home for Christmas—First Edition

The first Betsey Clark ball series ended in 1985, but this new one brings the artist's children back to the Keepsake line. Smaller in diameter, the balls in this second series show Betsey and her friends celebrating Christmas around the home. On the first ornament, they are busy decorating. Caption on Wall Poster: "May Christmas love fill every little corner of your world." On Calendar: "1986."

Pink Glass, 2⅞″ diam.
500QX277-6, $5.00 ☐

Windows of the World—Second Edition

A happy Dutch girl peeks over the half-door in her Holland home to greet the holiday. Someone has filled her little wooden shoes with Christmas goodies. "Vrolyk Kerstfeest 1986" is the Christmas greeting written above the door.

Handcrafted, 3″ tall
1000QX408-3, $10.00 ☐

Miniature Creche—Second Edition

Simple and elegant, this fine porcelain portrait of the Holy Family is second in the series of creches fashioned in different media. The velvety bisque of the figures contrasts beautifully with the satiny glow of the glazed arch. A brass star shines above.

Fine Porcelain, 3¾″ tall
900QX407-6, $9.00 ☐

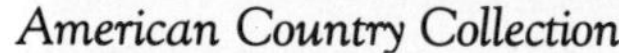

American Country Collection

Mr. and Mrs. Claus

Reindeer Champs, Betsey Clark: Home for Christmas, Windows of the World, Miniature Creche

Nostalgic Houses and Shops—Third Edition

What town would be complete without a "Christmas Candy Shoppe?" This ornament has two rooms: one downstairs where the sweets and confections are sold, and another upstairs, where the mixing and baking are done. A sign above the door says, "Candies 1986."

Handcrafted, 4⁵⁄₁₆" tall
1375QX403-3, $13.75 ☐

Wood Childhood Ornaments—Third Edition

This "Wooden Reindeer" takes a holiday ride on a wagon with wheels that turn. As he rolls along, he makes a galloping motion. The wagon is dated "1986."

Hand-Painted Wood, 2½" tall
750QX407-3, $7.50 ☐

Twelve Days of Christmas—Third Edition

On the third day of Christmas, three French hens nesting on holly leaves were etched onto a glowing acrylic teardrop. Gold foil-stamped caption reads, "The Twelve Days of Christmas 1986...Three French Hens."

Acrylic, 3⅜" tall
650QX378-6, $6.50 ☐

Nostalgic Houses and Shops, Wood Childhood Ornaments, Twelve Days of Christmas

Art Masterpiece—Third and Final Edition

This ornament is the last featuring classic paintings of the Madonna and Child reproduced on padded satin. Bezeled in brass, it carries the caption, "Lorenzo Di Cridi, Madonna and Child with the Infant St. John, The Nelson-Atkins Museum of Art, Kansas City, Missouri (Nelson Fund)."

Bezeled Satin, 3¼" tall
675QX350-6, $6.75 ☐

Porcelain Bear—Fourth Edition

"Cinnamon Bear" is carrying a surprise—a brightly wrapped Christmas package for a special friend. This fine porcelain ornament is painted by hand to accentuate the subtle detail.

Hand-Painted Fine Porcelain, 2¹¹⁄₁₆" tall
775QX405-6, $7.75 ☐

Tin Locomotive—Fifth Edition

The stencil-look holly design on the cabin of this pressed "Tin Locomotive" tell us the ornament is the Christmas Express. A mixture of interesting shapes and patterns, the train has wheels that turn as it rolls past your tree. It carries the date "1986."

Pressed Tin, 3¹⁷⁄₃₂" tall
1475QX403-6, $14.75 ☐

Art Masterpiece, Porcelain Bear, Tin Locomotive

Holiday Wildlife—Fifth Edition
While one Cedar Waxwing samples a berry, another looks on nearby. Framed in wood, this ornament presents a lifelike vision of nature. Caption: "Cedar Waxwing, (Cedarbird), BOMBYCILLA CEDORUM, Fifth in a series, Wildlife Collection, Christmas 1986."

Wood, 2½" diam.
750QX321-6, $7.50 ☐

Clothespin Soldier—Fifth Edition
Napoleon would have been proud to have this "French Officer" in his troop. Dressed in holiday colors and a hat decorated with holly, the soldier has movable arms.

Handcrafted, 1 27/32" tall
550QX406-3, $5.50 ☐

Rocking Horse—Sixth Edition
A golden palomino, with brown and blue saddle and trappings, is proud to ride on your tree this Christmas. He stands on sea-green rockers dated "1986" and has a flowing white yarn tail.

Handcrafted, 4" wide
1075QX401-6, $10.75 ☐

Norman Rockwell—Seventh Edition
Santa peers through his telescope to check up on all the good boys and girls before Christmas. Against the red background, the white bas-relief cameo has subtle variations in shading. Framed in brass, the ornament carries a gold foil-stamped caption on the back: "Checking Up, Seventh in a Series, Christmas 1986, The Norman Rockwell Collection."

Cameo, 3¼" diam.
775QX321-3, $7.75 ☐

Frosty Friends—Seventh Edition
This little Eskimo places a wreath around the neck of his new pal—a flocked baby reindeer whose antlers are just beginning to bud. They sit on a clear acrylic ice floe dated "1986."

Handcrafted, 2¼" tall
850QX405-3, $8.50 ☐

Here Comes Santa—Eighth Edition
A chrome bell announces that Santa has arrived with "Kringle's Kool Treats." The freezer advertises "Ice Cream" and "Snow Cones" made by "Kringle's," of course. Fitted with movable wheels, Santa's cart has a license plate dated "1986."

Handcrafted, 3 15/16" tall
1400QX404-3, $14.00 ☐

Thimble—Ninth Edition
This "Thimble Partridge" is sitting pretty. She has found the perfect nesting place atop a silvery thimble filled with holiday greenery and fruit.

Handcrafted, 1 21/32" tall
575QX406-6, $5.75 ☐

Holiday Wildlife, Clothespin Soldier, Rocking Horse

Norman Rockwell, Frosty Friends, Here Comes Santa, Thimble

THE 1987 COLLECTION

Three limited edition ornaments highlighted the 1987 Keepsake line. The annual fine porcelain limited edition, "Christmas Time Mime," is a combination of fantasy and tradition, limited to an edition size of 24,700.

The two other limited editions introduced new formats and new kinds of markings on the designs. "Christmas is Gentle," a basket holding two lambs, brought bone china into the line and was the first ornament to be individually numbered by hand. The number appears on the bottom of the basket along with the ornament's edition size of 24,700. The "Holiday Heirloom" ornament, a bell framed by a sculpted wreath, was the first limited edition Collectible Series, and the first design to feature silver plating and lead crystal. The edition size of 34,600 is embossed on a sculpted bow.

Designed for both plate and ornament collectors, the new "Collector's Plate" series began with a miniature porcelain plate decorated with artwork of children trimming the tree. The "Clothespin Soldier" series came to an end with the sixth edition — a "Sailor."

Three new collections of ornaments appeared in 1987. The designs in the new "Artists' Favorites" collection feature subject matter, such as bears and mice, that has been historically popular with collectors. These ornaments, however, are also favorites of the Hallmark artists who sculpted them. That's how the collection got its name! Each ornament carries the artist's signature or initials. The "Christmas Pizzazz" collection offers a lighthearted, contemporary look at the season. And the third group, the "Old-Fashioned Christmas" collection consists of traditional designs that look hand carved or homemade.

The Property ornaments in 1987 were integrated into other portions of the line such as "Holiday Humor." New properties were "Jammie Pies™," "Crayola®" and "Dr. Seuss." Back by popular demand were two satin balls — "Baby Boy" and "Baby Girl" for "Baby's First Christmas." The "Dad" ornament was humorous for the first time, and there was a special ornament for business use, "Holiday Greetings."

Commemoratives

Baby's First Christmas
Holding onto a tiny rattle, this baby has a lot of fun in the real spring seat swing. The ornament carries the caption, "Baby's First Christmas 1987," on the back of the seat.

Handcrafted, 4¼" tall
975QX411-3, $9.75 ☐

Baby's First Christmas Photoholder
An ecru fabric wreath, trimmed in lace and ribbon and embroidered with toys and holly, frames a favorite photo of Baby. "Baby's First Christmas 1987" is embroidered on the front, and a sentiment is silk-screened on the flocked back: "Welcome to Christmas, Baby dear. Everyone is glad you're here."

Fabric, 3¼" diam.
750QX461-9, $7.50 ☐

Baby's First Christmas
Baby's acrylic booties are decorated with etched jingle bells and holly. The caption, "Baby's First Christmas 1987," is stamped on the bow in gold foil.

Acrylic, 3½" tall
600QX372-9, $6.00 ☐

Baby's First Christmas: Handcrafted, Photoholder, Acrylic

Baby's First Christmas—Baby Girl
Dressed in rosy pink, the rag doll on this white satin ball is so proud she can spell "BABY GIRL" with her blocks. Caption: "A Baby Girl, so dear and sweet, makes your Christmas joy complete. Baby's First Christmas 1987."

White Satin, 2⅞" diam.
475QX274-7, $4.75 ☐

Baby's First Christmas—Baby Boy
A cuddly blue bear and a train carrying holly keep Baby's blocks from tumbling down. The blocks spell "BABY BOY," and the caption on this white satin ball reads, "A Baby Boy, so darling and dear, makes Christmas extra special this year. Baby's First Christmas 1987."

White Satin, 2⅞" diam.
475QX274-9, $4.75 ☐

Grandchild's First Christmas
A teddy bear plays with his blocks inside a jenny lind style playpen lined with a green and red quilt sprinkled with stars. The blanket carrying the caption, "Grandchild's First Christmas 1987," is made of fabric. The bottom of the ornament has room for personalization.

Handcrafted, 1¾" tall
900QX460-9, $9.00 ☐

Baby's Second Christmas
A cheery clown-in-the-box bounces on a real spring as he wishes Baby a happy holiday. Caption: "Baby's 2nd Christmas 1987." The ornament attaches to your tree with a special clip.

Handcrafted, 2¾" tall
575QX460-7, $5.75 ☐

Child's Third Christmas
Dressed in bright red with a real pompom on his cap, the child enjoys a holiday ride. The reindeer makes a galloping motion when it is tapped gently. Caption: "My 3rd Christmas 1987."

Handcrafted, 3" tall
575QX459-9, $5.75 ☐

Baby Locket
Baby's photo will look festive inside this special locket that has the shimmery look of silver. Embossed on the front is the word "Baby" and on the back, "1987." The locket has a special insert for personalization and comes with a wishbone hanger.

Textured Metal, 2¼" diam.
1500QX461-7, $15.00 ☐

Baby's First Christmas: Baby Girl, Baby Boy; Grandchild's First Christmas

Baby's Second Christmas, Child's Third Christmas, Baby Locket

Mother and Dad, Mother, Dad

Mother and Dad

Tied with a red satin ribbon, this deep blue porcelain bell carries a loving tribute: "For a Mother and Dad who give the gift of love. Christmas 1987." The tree on the front has a sponged stencil look.

Fine Porcelain, 4¾" tall
700QX462-7, $7.00 ☐

Mother

This acrylic oval's intricately cut beveled edge, a design seen for the first time in the Keepsake line, gives the ornament the look of cut glass. An etched sprig of holly accents the gold foil-stamped caption, "Mother is another word for love. Christmas 1987." The ornament is framed in brass.

Acrylic, 3½" tall
650QX373-7, $6.50 ☐

Dad

What does Dad want for Christmas? Another tie, of course! This polar bear has some special favorites—even one with a bright Hawaiian motif. Caption: "For Dad Christmas 1987."

Handcrafted, 3" tall
600QX462-9, $6.00 ☐

Husband

The sentiment and design on this ornament remind us that Christmas is the season of love and sharing. Against a sky blue background, the ivory cameo sleigh has delicate bas-relief detailing. Front Caption: "For My Husband." Back Caption: "The nicest part of Christmas is sharing it with you. 1987."

Cameo, 3¼" diam.
700QX373-9, $7.00 ☐

Sister

A lovely basket of poinsettias has been tied with a bright green bow especially for Sister. The design, a bright stencil look printed on wood, reflects the message on the back: "A Sister brings happiness wrapped in love. Christmas 1987."

Wood, 2¾" tall
600QX474-7, $6.00 ☐

Daughter

A pair of prancing reindeer pull a graceful swan sleigh, just like the ones seen in carousels. Fashioned to look like wood, the ornament carries the caption: "Daughter Christmas 1987."

Handcrafted, 1¼" tall
575QX463-7, $5.75 ☐

Son

This colorful train races across the tree to wish Son a happy holiday. It looks like an old-fashioned toy. Caption: "For Son Christmas 1987."

Handcrafted, 1" tall
575QX463-9, $5.75 ☐

Niece

Accented with touches of red, a flock of snowy white lambs frolic around a turquoise blue teardrop ball. The caption, printed in the lower border, reflects the cheery look of the design: "Christmas is happier...merrier...cheerier...because of a Niece's love. 1987."

Turquoise Blue Glass, 3" diam.
475QX275-9, $4.75 ☐

Grandmother

The loving caption on this frosted pink teardrop ball is illustrated with delicately painted roses and carnations. Caption: "Grandmothers, like flowers, fill the world with beauty, the heart with joy. Christmas 1987."

Pink Glass, 3" diam.
475QX277-9, $4.75 ☐

Grandparents

Building a snowman, skating on a frozen stream, and riding in a horse-drawn sleigh are just some of the activities depicted in this country portrait. The scene, reminiscent of American folk art, captures the warmth of the holiday and echoes the special message: "Grandparents...so warm, so loving, so like the Christmas season. 1987."

Porcelain White Glass, 2⅞" diam.
475QX277-7, $4.75 ☐

Grandson

Dressed in holiday uniforms, a musical marching band parades around this sky blue teardrop ball carrying a banner with a special message: "Grandsons have a talent for making wonderful memories." The drum reads, "Christmas 1987."

Sky Blue Glass, 3" diam.
475QX276-9, $4.75 ☐

Granddaughter

Filled with toys, the antique sleigh on this padded satin ornament offers a nostalgic look at the joys of the holiday. The ornament is bezeled in brass and carries the caption, "A Granddaughter makes each day a holiday in the heart. Christmas 1987."

Bezeled Satin, 2¾" diam.
600QX374-7, $6.00 ☐

Godchild

This vivid blue ball looks as if it were sprinkled with snow. The brightly lit holiday tree on the front, designed to resemble torn paper, symbolizes the warmth of the season and reflects the caption: "A Godchild makes Christmas glow a little brighter. 1987."

Blue Glass, 2⅞" diam.
475QX276-7, $4.75 ☐

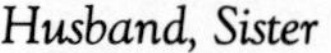
Husband, Sister

Daughter, Son, Niece

Grandmother, Grandparents

Grandson, Granddaughter, Godchild

First Christmas Together
Displayed open or closed, this heart-shaped brass locket is a loving memento of the season. Embossed lovebirds decorate the back, and the embossed caption, "First Christmas Together 1987," adorns the front. The ornament comes with a wishbone hanger.

Textured Brass, 2¼" tall
1500QX446-9, $15.00 ☐

First Christmas Together
Home is where the heart is, especially in this Alpine cottage captioned, "First Christmas Together 1987." The room inside holds a bottle-brush tree and a sampler with, "Love Sweet Love."

Handcrafted, 3" tall
950QX446-7, $9.50 ☐

First Christmas Together
Two raccoons snuggle inside a fabric sweatshirt with "First Christmas Together" silk-screened on the front. The date "1987" appears inside a heart on the back.

Handcrafted, 2½" tall
800QX445-9, $8.00 ☐

First Christmas Together
Two exquisitely etched swans float across an acrylic oval framed in brass. The caption, stamped in gold foil, says "First Christmas Together 1987."

Acrylic, 2½" tall
650QX371-9, $6.50 ☐

First Christmas Together
A garden of pastel poinsettias touched with silver decorates this frosted white glass ball. Two lovebirds appear on the front with the caption, "First Christmas Together 1987." On Back: "To all who love, love is all the world."

White Glass, 2⅞" diam.
475QX272-9, $4.75 ☐

Ten Years Together
A heart-shaped floral wreath frames the caption "Ten Years Together" on this snow white porcelain bell. The ornament is tied with a bright red satin ribbon and carries "Christmas 1987" on the back.

Fine Porcelain, 4¾" tall
700QX444-7, $7.00 ☐

Twenty-Five Years Together
A crisply painted pair of cardinals enjoys the holiday season on a miniature porcelain collector's plate that celebrates a life of sharing. The lettering on front and back is printed in traditional silver. Front Caption: "25 Years Together Christmas 1987." Back: "Love is for always." Plate stand included.

Fine Porcelain, 3¼" diam.
750QX443-9, $7.50 ☐

First Christmas Together: Textured Brass, Handcrafted, Handcrafted, Acrylic

Fifty Years Together
The velvety bisque finish of this unique porcelain bell contrasts beautifully with the glazed finish of the bas-relief poinsettia design and sculpted handle. "Fifty Years Together" and "Christmas 1987" are printed in gold.

Fine Porcelain, 5" tall
800QX443-7, $8.00 ☐

Word of Love
There's no other word that means so much. This fine bisque porcelain ornament is accented with touches of gold and a tiny red dangling heart. Caption: "Christmas 1987."

Fine Porcelain, 2⅛" tall
800QX447-7, $8.00 ☐

Heart in Blossom
A single rose is a timeless symbol of love. It has been carefully etched into this heart-shaped acrylic ornament to reflect the message stamped in gold foil: "Love is the heart in blossom. Christmas 1987."

Acrylic, 2¾" tall
600QX372-7, $6.00 ☐

Sweetheart
A package labeled "For My Sweetheart" is about to be delivered in this surrey with the fabric fringe on top. Beautifully detailed, the vehicle has wheels that turn and room for personalization underneath. "Christmas 1987" is printed in gold on the front of the surrey, and the word "Sweet" printed above two entwined hearts appears on the back.

Handcrafted, 3⅛" tall
1100QX447-9, $11.00 ☐

Love Is Everywhere
Against a shiny chrome background, a winter landscape echoes the peace and serenity of the holiday season. A pair of cardinals brings a bright splash of color to the silvery sky. Caption: "Beautifully, peacefully, Christmas touches our lives...love is everywhere. 1987."

Chrome and Frosted Blue Glass, 2⅞" diam.
475QX278-7, $4.75 ☐

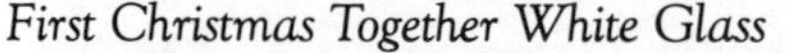
First Christmas Together White Glass

Ten Years Together, Twenty-Five Years Together, Fifty Years Together

Word of Love, Heart in Blossom

Sweetheart, Love is Everywhere

Holiday Greetings

This elegant ornament features a graphic silver Christmas tree and lettering against a shimmery blue and violet foil background. Bezeled in chrome, the ornament has been designed to be especially appropriate for use by businesses. The ornament box provides room for personalization. Caption on Front: "Season's Greetings." On Back: "Wishing you happiness at this beautiful time of year. 1987."

Bezeled Foil, 2¾" diam.
600QX375-7, $6.00 ☐

Warmth of Friendship

The gold foil caption stamped on this acrylic ornament displays the classic beauty of calligraphy. Caption: "As Christmas warms the world friendship warms our hearts. 1987."

Acrylic 3¾" tall
600QX375-9, $6.00 ☐

Time for Friends

Two white mice hang garland around a red glass teardrop ball. They're hurrying to meet each other in the center because the caption says, "When good friends meet, good times are complete! Christmas 1987."

Red Glass, 3" diam.
475QX280-7, $4.75 ☐

From Our Home to Yours

A friendly welcome awaits you at every door in this neighborhood. Decorated for the holidays, the doors circle a frosted white glass teardrop ball that carries the caption, "From Our Home...To Yours...At Christmas 1987."

White Glass, 3" diam.
475QX279-9, $4.75 ☐

New Home

The scene on this ornament brings back memories of holidays long ago, but the format is new to the Keepsake line. Printed in white on a mirrored acrylic background is a snug and cozy cottage. Caption: "A New Home is a wonderful beginning to wonderful memories. Christmas 1987."

Mirrored Acrylic, 2¾" diam.
600QX376-7, $6.00 ☐

Babysitter

The scenes on this porcelain white teardrop ball symbolize the love given to children by those special people who take care of them. One bunny is reading a book titled "Bunny Tales," and a calendar on the wall says it's "1987." Caption: "For bringing children such special gifts...gentleness, caring, and love. Merry Christmas."

Porcelain White Glass, 3" diam.
475QX279-7, $4.75 ☐

Holiday Greetings, Warmth of Friendship, Time for Friends

From Our Home to Yours, New Home, Babysitter

Teacher

This beary good student has a message for teacher and room for personalization on his slate: "Merry Christmas, Teacher From (name)." But the bear can be mischievous since he carved "1987" into the desk.

Handcrafted, 2″ tall
575QX466-7, $5.75 ☐

Holiday Humor

SNOOPY® and WOODSTOCK

SNOOPY® and WOODSTOCK have decorated a bottle-brush tree for the holiday. WOODSTOCK perches on top—the perfect angel. On Dish: "SNOOPY."

Handcrafted, 2½″ tall
725QX472-9, $7.25 ☐

Bright Christmas Dreams

Wearing colorful nightcaps, four mice dream of a bright Christmas in an authentic Crayola® box made of varnished paper. Front of Box: "Crayola® Crayons, Bright Christmas Dreams, Binney & Smith®." Back, Sides and Bottom of Box: "Crayola® Crayons." The back of the box also carries the caption, "Christmas 1987" designed to look like part of a store code.

Handcrafted, 4″ tall
725QX473-7, $7.25 ☐

Joy Ride

Santa and a reindeer take a holiday spin on Santa's new motorcyle. The "wheels" really do spin and the reindeer wears a fabric muffler. Caption on Front Fender: "Joy Ride." On License Plate: "1987."

Handcrafted, 3½″ tall
1150QX440-7, $11.50 ☐

Pretty Kitty

This little kitten is all tangled up in some red beads. He has to hold on tight because he's the clapper inside the clear glass bell.

Handcrafted, Glass, 3½″ tall
1100QX448-9, $11.00 ☐

Santa at the Bat

Santa is the star of the team because his signature "Santa Claus" bat connects with a pearlized snowball. His uniform reads: "North Pole Nicks 87."

Handcrafted, 3¼″ tall
775QX457-9, $7.75 ☐

Jogging Through the Snow

Carrying his radio and wearing headphones, this rabbit listens to Christmas music, of course. His shirt carries his number "87" and "Holiday Run."

Handcrafted, 3″ tall
725QX457-7, $7.25 ☐

Teacher

SNOOPY®, Bright Christmas Dreams

Joy Ride, Pretty Kitty, Santa at the Bat, Jogging Through the Snow

Jack Frosting
Jack dips his brush into an acorn filled with sparkling frost and brushes the glitter onto each leaf, creating a winter wonderland for all to enjoy. This ornament attaches to your tree with a special clip.

Handcrafted, 2½" tall
700QX449-9, $7.00 ☐

Raccoon Biker
This fellow rides the trails on his dirt bike to deliver a Christmas gift cross country. The front of the bike is marked "87."

Handcrafted, 3" tall
700QX458-7, $7.00 ☐

Treetop Dreams
The squirrel was nestled all snug in his bed while visions of acorns danced in his head! His blanket is polka dot fabric, and a matching fabric ribbon decorates the wreath. To achieve an especially authentic look, real sticks were used to mold this design.

Handcrafted, 3" tall
675QX459-7, $6.75 ☐

Night Before Christmas
It's the night before Christmas, and this mouse isn't stirring. He'd much rather be sleeping in Santa's hat. The flocked hat has furry trim and a pompom at the top. A tiny chunk of cheese is tucked into the trim at the back.

Handcrafted, 2¾" tall
650QX451-7, $6.50 ☐

"Owliday" Wish
Wearing brass spectacles, this owl helps us all get a clear vision of his "owliday" wish on the eyechart: "SEASONS GREETINGS TO YOU." Real sticks were used to mold his perch and pointer.

Handcrafted, 2" tall
650QX455-9, $6.50 ☐

Let It Snow
This little tyke is dressed for cold weather—but he won't feel it wearing his knitted cap and muffler and real pompom earmuffs.

Handcrafted, 3" tall
650QX458-9, $6.50 ☐

Hot Dogger
Santa is king of the hill, a champion skier and, as his ski jacket says, a "Hot Dogger" on the slopes! His ski outfit is decorated with snowflake patches.

Handcrafted, 2½" tall
650QX471-9, $6.50 ☐

Spots 'n Stripes
Santa has left a special gift in this Dalmatian pup's Christmas stocking—a candy cane made to order in his favorite shape.

Handcrafted, 2¼" tall
550QX452-9, $5.50 ☐

Jack Frosting, Raccoon Biker, Treetop Dreams, Night Before Christmas

"Owliday" Wish, Let It Snow, Hot Dogger, Spots 'n Stripes

Seasoned Greetings

This elf has a very important job to do—placing salt on all the holiday pretzels. He uses a silvery shaker that he fills from his salt bag labeled, "Seasoned Greetings SALT."

Handcrafted, 2" tall
625QX454-9, $6.25 ☐

Chocolate Chipmunk

Has this chipmunk confiscated a chip from his cookie, or is he looking for a place to add one chip more? He'll never tell! He's dressed for the winter in a knitted red muffler. A real cookie was used to mold the design, and the ornament attaches with a special clip.

Handcrafted, 2" tall
600QX456-7, $6.00 ☐

Fudge Forever

Sitting in a dark blue spatterware ladle, this little mouse is so full of fudge he can hardly budge! But that doesn't stop him from scooping up just a little bit more with his own mouse-sized spoon.

Handcrafted, 3" tall
500QX449-7, $5.00 ☐

Seasoned Greetings, Chocolate Chipmunk, Fudge Forever

Sleepy Santa

If there's one person who deserves a nap after Christmas—it's Santa. He lounges in his favorite chair, soaking his feet and dreaming of next year's toys. The chair is flocked and the calendar page reads, "DEC. 26."

Handcrafted, 2¾" tall
625QX450-7, $6.25 ☐

Reindoggy

This little puppy may be wearing antlers, but his expression shows he isn't ready to pull Santa's sleigh. The antlers were molded from real sticks and are tied to the puppy's head with a red satin bow.

Handcrafted, 2¾" tall
575QX452-7, $5.75 ☐

Christmas Cuddle

Wearing matching Santa hats in honor of the holiday, these two buddies enjoy a warm Christmas hug. The kitten's hat is topped with a real pompom.

Handcrafted, 2¾" tall
575QX453-7, $5.75 ☐

Paddington™ Bear

Paddington™ likes to eat what he bakes! Perhaps he has flavored the cookies with his favorite food—honey. He wears a red apron marked "Paddington™ Bear" and a chef's hat tagged, "Please look after this Bear Thank You."

Handcrafted, 3" tall
550QX472-7, $5.50 ☐

Sleepy Santa, Reindoggy, Christmas Cuddle, Paddington™ Bear

Nature's Decorations
The painted animals and birds on this light blue glass ball are Mother Nature's way of decorating her wintry world. Caption: "The nicest Christmas decorations start with Nature's own creations. 1987."

Blue Glass, 2⅞" diam.
475QX273-9, $4.75 ☐

Dr. Seuss: The Grinch's Christmas
Framed by a colorful Christmas wreath, the Grinch is smiling at last. He and a chorus of Whos from Who-ville celebrate the holiday on a blue glass ball. Caption: "A very merry wish for a merry, merry Christmas."

Blue Glass, 2⅞" diam.
475QX278-3, $4.75 ☐

Jammie Pies™
A new Hallmark property, Jammie Pies™, makes its Keepsake debut on this porcelain white glass ball. The swan arrives from the "Land of Sweet Dreams" bringing the child a visitor—a Jammie Pies friend who knows a world of stories. Caption: "When Jammie Pies are close to you, all your Christmas dreams come true. 1987."

Porcelain White Glass, 2⅞" diam.
475QX283-9, $4.75 ☐

PEANUTS®
Wearing their cool dark glasses, SNOOPY®, WOODSTOCK and his friends, and even a snowman show that the caption on this chrome teardrop ball tells the truth: "Everyone's cool at Christmastime!" The supper dish carries the date "1987."

Chrome Glass, 3" diam.
475QX281-9, $4.75 ☐

Happy Santa
Carrying a shiny brass bell, Santa uses his candy cane to swing from a branch on your tree.

Handcrafted, 2½" tall
475QX456-9, $4.75 ☐

Icy Treat
This penguin knows what's good to eat—especially in the cool North Pole. His shimmery cherry treat is just the thing for a frosty afternoon snack.

Handcrafted, 2¼" tall
450QX450-9, $4.50 ☐

Mouse in the Moon
Reissue from 1986. (See 1986 Annual Collection.)

Handcrafted, 2¾" tall
550QX416-6, $5.50

L'il Jingler
Reissue from 1986. (See 1986 Annual Collection.)

Handcrafted, 2" tall
675QX419-3, $6.75

Nature's Decorations, Dr. Seuss: The Grinch's Christmas, Jammie Pies™

PEANUTS®, Happy Santa, Icy Treat

Walnut Shell Rider
Reissue from 1986. (See 1986 Annual Collection.)

Handcrafted, 1¾" tall
600QX419-6, $6.00

Treetop Trio
Reissue from 1986. (See 1986 Annual Collection.)

Handcrafted, 2" tall
1100QX425-6, $11.00

Jolly Hiker
Reissue from 1986. (See 1986 Annual Collection.)

Handcrafted, 2" tall
500QX483-2, $5.00

Merry Koala
Reissue from 1986. (See 1986 Annual Collection.)

Handcrafted, 2" tall
500QX415-3, $5.00

Old-Fashioned Christmas Collection

Nostalgic Rocker
Looking as if it were crafted by hand, this subtly painted pony is fashioned of wood and has fabric ears. The clean lines and simple design reflect an American Country styling.

Wood, 2½″ tall
650QX468-9, $6.50 ☐

Little Whittler
The little carver prides himself on the craftsmanship he puts into the reindeer toy he is carving. This ornament, sculpted and painted to resemble carved wood, displays the same craftsmanship and a touch of whimsy.

Handcrafted, 3″ tall
600QX469-9, $6.00 ☐

Country Wreath
The warm old-fashioned design of this straw wreath reminds us of Christmas in the country. Tied with burgundy yarn, the ornament is decorated with tiny wooden hearts and trees and a wooden house.

Wood and Straw, 4¾″ tall
575QX470-9, $5.75 ☐

In a Nutshell
There's a world of Christmas inside this nutshell. Two intricately detailed scenes show a teddy bear beneath a Christmas tree and a fireplace with two tiny stockings. Molded from a real walnut, the ornament is hinged so it can be displayed open and stored closed.

Handcrafted, 1½″ tall
550QX469-7, $5.50 ☐

Folk Art Santa
Carefully painted and antiqued, this Old-World Santa reflects the rich tradition of folk art. His deeply sculpted face and beard and the details of his clothing give him the appearance of hand-carved wood. Carrying a bottle-brush tree, he wears a long coat accented with touches of gold.

Handcrafted, 4″ tall
525QX474-9, $5.25 ☐

Nostalgic Rocker, Little Whittler

Country Wreath, In a Nutshell, Folk Art Santa

Christmas Pizzazz Collection

Doc Holiday
Santa becomes a hero of the Old West when he rides the spring-powered mechanical reindeer. When you set the ornament on a mantel or table and gently tap it, Santa gets a bouncy ride. His cowboy shirt carries his name, "Doc Holiday."

Handcrafted, 4" tall
800QX467-7, $8.00 ☐

Christmas Fun Puzzle
A favorite childhood puzzle is updated in a whimsical ball ornament. Divided horizontally into three movable sections, this blue ball is decorated with three bas-relief figures—Santa, mouse and reindeer. As you turn the sections, you mix the top, middle and bottom parts of the figures creating new characters such as a Rein-mouse or a Santa-deer.

Handcrafted, 2½" diam.
800QX467-9, $8.00 ☐

Jolly Follies
Dressed in tuxes and tails, three dapper penguins actually kick up their heels and dance each time you pull the string. The sparkling acrylic stage carries the name of their act, "Jolly Follies."

Handcrafted, 2" tall
850QX466-9, $8.50 ☐

St. Louie Nick
He's cool, he's hot, he's a jazzy dresser from his beret to his spats. Santa blows the sweetest horn this side of the North Pole and wears a vest with his stage name, "St. Louie Nick."

Handcrafted, 3½" tall
775QX453-9, $7.75 ☐

Holiday Hourglass
Designed to be displayed in two different ways, this realistic hourglass celebrates both Christmas and the New Year. Through Christmas Day, the ornament can be displayed so that the "Merry Christmas" wish and snowman in Santa cap appear. After Christmas, the hourglass can be flipped over to display the snowman in top hat and "Happy New Year" wish.

Handcrafted, 3" tall
800QX470-7, $8.00 ☐

Doc Holiday, Christmas Fun Puzzle

Jolly Follies, St. Louie Nick, Holiday Hourglass

Mistletoad
You don't have to kiss this whimsical fellow to get a special Christmas surprise. When you pull the cord, he gives you a wide holiday grin and a loud greeting in a very froggy voice. His hat is decorated with a pompom and his name, "Mistletoad."

Handcrafted, 3¾" tall
700QX468-7, $7.00 ☐

Happy Holidata
Two little programmers watch the message "Happy Holidata" flash onto the computer screen in alternating colors of green and red. On the back of the terminal, the name "Cranberry Computer" tells you this ornament is a high-tech edition.

Handcrafted, 1½" tall
650QX471-7, $6.50 ☐

Traditional Ornaments

Goldfinch
This realistic Goldfinch looks as if he has paused in flight to admire the scenery below. Fashioned of fine porcelain, he has been painted by hand to accentuate detail. Unlike the previous porcelain birds in the Keepsake line, this ornament attaches to your tree with a traditional hook instead of a clip.

Hand-Painted Fine Porcelain, 2½" tall
700QX464-9, $7.00 ☐

Heavenly Harmony
This little angel brings Christmas music for all the world to hear. Reminiscent of an Old-World Spanish belltower, the ornament plays "Joy to the World." The music is started by a key at the back.

Musical, Handcrafted, 4¼" tall
1500QX465-9, $15.00 ☐

Special Memories Photoholder
Both needlepoint and embroidery decorate the front of this bright holiday wreath. Trimmed in lace, it will display one of your cherished photographs. The wreath hangs from a green satin ribbon accented with a red satin rosette. Caption on Back: "Every Christmas brings special moments to remember. 1987."

Fabric, 3¼" diam.
675QX464-7, $6.75 ☐

Joyous Angels
Three intricately sculpted angels join hands and dance their joy beneath a brass star. Their halos and the trim on their snowy white dresses are touched with gold.

Handcrafted, 4" tall
775QX465-7, $7.75 ☐

Mistletoad, Happy Holidata

Goldfinch, Heavenly Harmony, Special Memories Photoholder, Joyous Angels

Promise of Peace

Carrying a gold foil olive branch, the Christmas dove spreads a timeless message of the season. To enhance the dimension of the design, the dove was etched into the back of the acrylic piece and the caption into the front, along the bevel. The ornament is framed in brass. Caption: "a season of hope, a reminder of miracles, a promise of peace."

Acrylic, 2¾" diam.
650QX374-9, $6.50 ☐

Christmas Keys

A miniature upright piano, decorated with festive green and red holly, brings to mind those happy times spent caroling with family and friends. The music is captioned, "Carols."

Handcrafted, 2" tall
575QX473-9, $5.75 ☐

I Remember Santa

Taken from the Hallmark Historical Collection, three antique post card paintings are reproduced on this porcelain white glass ball. They offer a vision of Santa Claus that brings back memories of Christmas long ago. Caption: "At Christmastime, especially, those magic memories start...those memories of yesterday that so delight the heart. 1987."

Porcelain White Glass, 2⅞" diam.
475QX278-9, $4.75 ☐

Norman Rockwell: Christmas Scenes

A hearty toast, a joyful dance, a stolen kiss under the mistletoe—all of these are depicted with warmth and gentle humor in the Norman Rockwell paintings on this gold glass ball. The three "Christmas Scenes" come from the Hallmark Collection of Norman Rockwell originals. Caption: "O gather friends, at Christmastime, to sing a song of cheer, to reminisce the days gone by, to toast the bright new year. From the Norman Rockwell Collection 1987."

Gold Glass, 2⅞" diam.
475QX282-7, $4.75 ☐

Currier & Ives: American Farm Scene

Porcelain white glass is the perfect setting for this nostalgic portrait of a wintry morning on the farm. The caption is decorated with painted holly and ribbon. Caption: "Christmas 1987, American Farm Scene, Currier & Ives."

Porcelain White Glass, 2⅞" diam.
475QX282-9, $4.75 ☐

Promise of Peace, Christmas Keys

I Remember Santa, Norman Rockwell, Currier & Ives

Limited Editions

Christmas Time Mime

Wearing a Santa hat and beard, the mime shares a moment of Christmas with a friend. His bag, tied with a golden chain, is filled with stars and magic. This ornament, made of fine porcelain and painted by hand, is limited to an edition size of 24,700 pieces. A wooden display stand is included in the box as well as the following poem that tells a charming story about the design:

The Mime looks deep in the
teddy bear's eyes.
The teddy bear looks at the Mime,
And they feel they have known each other
From some other place and time.
There's a magical bond between them
From the silent world they share,
And now they know, wherever one goes,
The other will always be there.

Hand-Painted Fine Porcelain, 2½" tall
2750QX442-9, $27.50 □

Christmas is Gentle

Two little lambs...one fast asleep...the other ready to play...embody the gentle spirit of the season. This ornament, issued in an edition limited to 24,700 pieces, is the first in the Keepsake line to be individually numbered by hand. It is made of white bone china accented with gold and subtle touches of color. Caption on the Bottom: "Christmas is gentle, Bone China, Limited Edition of 24,700 Max., Number: (hand-written number)."

Hand-Painted Bone China, 3" tall
1750QX444-9, $17.50 □

Christmas Time Mime, Christmas is Gentle

Special Edition

Favorite Santa

Like previous Special Edition ornaments, this one is designed for display on table or mantel as well as the tree. Fashioned of fine porcelain and painted by hand, Santa carries a long, long stocking which is the subject of the following legend printed on a card tucked into the ornament box:

One day Old St. Nick found a stocking—
It was threadbare, and tattered, and torn,
But his elves fixed it up with their magic,
And a new Christmas legend was born.
They say that it's loaded with presents
That are tied up with ribbons and bows;
For each gift he gives, a new one appears,
How it works—only Santa Claus knows!

Hand-Painted Fine Porcelain, 5½" tall
2250QX445-7, $22.50 □

Favorite Santa

Artists' Favorites

Three Men in a Tub

Inside the tub the famous trio—butcher, baker and candlestick maker—hold sausages, a cake with holly icing, and a Christmas candle. Donna Lee, the sculptor of this ornament, likes to bring classic nursery ryhmes to life with a contemporary look that is often whimsical. The tub looks like wood and carries the caption, "Rub-A-Dub-Dub."

Handcrafted, 3" tall
Artist: Donna Lee
800QX454-7, $8.00 ☐

Wee Chimney Sweep

Artist Ed Seale's mouse sweeps the chimney so Santa will stay neat and clean on Christmas Eve. A hard worker, the mouse carries a real brush. Seale commented that his design reflects the increased use of fireplaces and woodburning stoves to keep homes warm in the winter.

Handcrafted, 3" tall
Artist: Ed Seale
625QX451-9, $6.25 ☐

December Showers

Sitting on an acrylic cloud, this angel stays dry under her holly-trimmed umbrella. She checks to see if the shower has stopped because she wants to play. Artist Donna Lee designed the angel to resemble a real child—full of fun and mischief.

Handcrafted, 2½" tall
Artist: Donna Lee
550QX448-7, $5.50 ☐

Beary Special

This cuddly flocked bear reaches up to put his ornament on your tree. It's a tiny green ball decorated with his own likeness. Artist Bob Siedler explained that he likes sculpting bears because they are his daughter's favorite and part of everyone's childhood memories.

Handcrafted, 2½" tall
Artist: Bob Siedler
475QX455-7, $4.75 ☐

Collectible Series

Holiday Heirloom—First Edition/Limited Edition

This elegant new series introduces lead crystal and a precious metal into the Keepsake line. The intricately sculpted wreath has been plated in silver and frames a bell made of 24 percent lead crystal with a silver-plated holly clapper inside. The series also is the first to be offered in a limited edition. The date "1987" is embossed on the front of the wreath, and the edition size is embossed on the back: "Limited Edition 34,600."

Lead Crystal, Silver Plating, 3¼" tall
2500QX485-7, $25.00 ☐

Three Men in a Tub, Wee Chimney Sweep

December Showers, Beary Special

Holiday Heirloom

Collector's Plate—First Edition

The first collector's plate, issued in the late 1800s, offered a beautiful Christmas scene. This new ornament continues that meaningful tradition in miniature plates fashioned of fine porcelain. Each edition will bring a vision of children celebrating the season and a message on the back. The first plate shows children decorating the family tree. Caption: "Light Shines at Christmas. 1987." Plate stand included.

Fine Porcelain, 3¼″ diam.
800QX481-7, $8.00 ☐

Mr. and Mrs. Claus—Second Edition

Mrs. Claus baked her spouse a plateful of cookies to give him energy for his Christmas Eve ride. His calendar reads, "1987 Dec. 24," so it's almost time to go. But Santa won't leave without his snack because he knows there's nothing better than "Home Cooking."

Handcrafted, 3″ tall
1325QX483-7, $13.25 ☐

Reindeer Champs—Second Edition

Warmly dressed in a skating sweater monogrammed with her name "Dancer" and the date "'87," this reindeer is a star on ice. She whirls and twirls on skates trimmed with real pompoms.

Handcrafted, 3½″ tall
750QX480-9, $7.50 ☐

Betsey Clark: Home for Christmas—Second Edition

While Santa peers around the porch of the house addressed "1987," Betsey and her friends trim the outdoor trees and paint holiday messages on the windows. One window says, "There's no place like Christmas," and the other reads, "Noel."

Gold Glass, 2⅞″ diam.
500QX272-7, $5.00 ☐

Windows of the World—Third Edition

Sitting by the sea, a little Polynesian child strums a holiday tune on her ukulele. She has written "1987" in the sand and hung her stocking out for Santa. Her thatched window seat carries the Christmas greeting, "Mele Kalikimaka."

Handcrafted, 3″ tall
1000QX482-7, $10.00 ☐

Miniature Creche—Third Edition

Multiple layers of delicately etched brass, washed in gold, nickel and copper, create a stunning three-dimensional Nativity. Gold wire starbeams shine on the Holy Family from a Christmas star above the stable.

Multi-Plated Brass, 3½″ tall
900QX481-9, $9.00 ☐

Collector's Plate, Mr. and Mrs. Claus, Reindeer Champs

Betsey Clark: Home for Christmas, Windows of the World, Miniature Creche

Nostalgic Houses and Shops—Fourth Edition
The Victorian "House on Main St." has an exclusive "1987" address. Its spacious upstairs bedroom is decorated in shades of lavender and mauve; the downstairs parlor has a blue chair, matching drapes and a tiny bottle-brush Christmas tree.

Handcrafted, 4¼" tall
1400QX483-9, $14.00 □

Twelve Days of Christmas—Fourth Edition
Four etched colly birds gather in the center of a beveled acrylic diamond because it is the fourth day of Christmas. Stamped in gold foil, the caption reads, "The Twelve Days of Christmas 1987...four colly birds..." The four classic acrylic shapes used in this series—quadrafoil, heart, teardrop and diamond—will be repeated three times.

Acrylic, 4" tall
650QX370-9, $6.50 □

Wood Childhood Ornaments—Fourth Edition
Saddled in festive green and red and carefully groomed from his plush mane to his yarn tail, this "Wooden Horse" is ready to lead the Christmas parade. His cart has wheels that turn as he is pulled along. He is dated "1987."

Wood, 2¼" tall
750QX441-7, $7.50 □

Nostalgic Houses and Shops, Twelve Days of Christmas, Wood Childhood Ornaments

Porcelain Bear—Fifth Edition
What is "Cinnamon Bear" searching for inside his Christmas stocking? Maybe he'll find some honey candy stuck in the toe! Made of fine porcelain, the ornament has been painted by hand.

Hand-Painted Fine Porcelain, 2⅞" tall
775QX442-7, $7.75 □

Tin Locomotive—Sixth Edition
Ringing its brass bell and chugging along on wheels that actually roll, this Tin Locomotive ornament arrives at the North Pole station. The spoke pattern of the large rear wheels resembles a circle of cut-out hearts. The train is dated "1987."

Pressed Tin, 3½" tall
1475QX484-9, $14.75 □

Holiday Wildlife—Sixth Edition
Framed in wood, two snow geese fly across the starry Christmas sky, creating a picture of beauty and grace. The caption on the back reads, "Snow Goose, CHEN HYPERBOREA, Sixth in a Series, Wildlife Collection, Christmas 1987."

Wood, 2½" diam.
750QX371-7, $7.50 □

Porcelain Bear, Tin Locomotive, Holiday Wildlife

Clothespin Soldier—Sixth and Final Edition
Fashioned with movable arms, this "Sailor" in a crisp white uniform signals all hands on deck to bid farewell to the Clothespin series. His signals are easy to see because his flags display bright green trees against a red background.

Handcrafted, 2¼ " tall
550QX480-7, $5.50 ☐

Frosty Friends—Eighth Edition
This little flocked seal has jumped up through a hole in the ice to deliver a gift to his Eskimo friend. He's carrying the package the best way he can—balancing it ever so carefully on his nose. The ice is made of clear acrylic and the package is dated "1987."

Handcrafted, 2 " tall
850QX440-9, $8.50 ☐

Rocking Horse—Seventh Edition
A fitting steed for any prince or princess, this white charger is saddled in red, blue and gold and rides on royal purple rockers dated "1987." His mane and graceful yarn tail are the color of cream.

Handcrafted, 3¾ " wide
1075QX482-9, $10.75 ☐

Norman Rockwell—Eighth Edition
Norman Rockwell is one of America's most beloved artists. His delightful painting of a little girl dancing with her dog has been transformed into a delicate bas-relief cameo against a light blue background. Framed in chrome, the ornament carries the caption, "The Christmas Dance, Eighth in a Series, Christmas 1987, The Norman Rockwell Collection."

Cameo, 3¼ " diam.
775QX370-7, $7.75 ☐

Here Comes Santa—Ninth Edition
All the toys are packed, and Santa is driving through town in his sporty new car. "Santa's Woody" has whitewalls that turn, custom paneling, and two personalized license plates. The rear plate carries the date "1987," and the front one conveys Santa's special wish: "JOY-2-U."

Handcrafted, 2 " tall
1400QX484-7, $14.00 ☐

Thimble—Tenth Edition
A bunny plays his silvery thimble drum to celebrate the tenth year of this series. The "Thimble Drummer" has a fluffy pompom tail, and the strap around his drum is made of striped fabric ribbon.

Handcrafted, 2 " tall
575QX441-9, $5.75 ☐

Clothespin Soldier, Frosty Friends, Rocking Horse

Norman Rockwell, Here Comes Santa, Thimble

KEEPSAKE MAGIC LIGHTED ORNAMENTS

Of all the changes that have occurred in ornaments over the years, none has been more exciting, and created more enthusiasm among collectors than Hallmark's introduction of lighted and motion ornaments. Hallmark's innovation represented another step in the continually evolving tradition of lighting a Christmas tree.

It all began in the early 1800s, when trees were illuminated by candlelight. Candles were attached ever so carefully to the tree to avoid burning the branches, touching other decorations, and toppling over.

With Thomas Edison's invention of the light bulb in 1879 came another change — electric lights! The first electric Christmas tree lights (80 in all) were shown in a private home in New York City in 1882. At this time, however, only the wealthy could afford electric lights.

As electric lighting became more widespread, so did electric Christmas tree lights. Those first simple yet expensive glass bulbs evolved into the affordable, multi-colored miniature lights so popular today. Now, three out of every four Christmas trees are lighted.

In 1984, Hallmark added their contribution to our ever evolving tradition with the introduction of Lighted Ornaments. In 1986, Hallmark came up with even more innovations — ornaments with holograms, changing scenes and motion!

The hologram technique uses laser photography to transform a flat image into one that looks three-dimensional. This was first used in the 1986 design, "Santa's On His Way," where Santa and his sleigh seem to sail over a city skyline.

Hallmark artist Donna Lee originated the "changing scene" effect through the use of alternating lights. After a light illuminates the first scene inside the panorama ball, additional lights come on, causing the second scene to appear as if by magic.

With the advent of all this new technology came a concentration on teamwork between Hallmark's artists and engineers. Nowhere is this more apparent than in the "light and motion" ornaments such as the 1986 "Village Express."

Keepsake Magic Ornaments bring wonder to Christmas.

The artist must design the ornament to accommodate a motor and gear box that govern the motion. Once the ornament is designed, the engineer develops the circuitry to move the pieces inside the ornament properly. Because the two go hand-in-hand, the design and engineering continually evolve until the whole package is finalized.

Yet another innovation occurred in 1987 — blinking lights. In the "Good Cheer Blimp," a circle of lights blinks on and off around the words, "Good Cheer." In both "blinking light" and "changing scene" ornaments, a circuit board is implanted inside the design to assure the proper timing of lights to create the special effects.

Hallmark tests every Keepsake Magic Ornament for as many as 10,000 hours in their own laboratory. Each design must pass rigorous tests for durability and safety, or it is cancelled or completely redesigned until it passes.

The innovations in the Keepsake Magic line have sped the evolution of Christmas tree lighting to its present state. With Hallmark's goal to create ornaments that are beautiful, unique, safe and innovative, I suspect Keepsake Magic ornaments will evolve even further in the future.

Mr. Edison, you'd be proud.

THE 1984
LIGHTED ORNAMENT COLLECTION

Ornament collectors surged with excitement as Lighted Ornaments were introduced by Hallmark in 1984. This marked the first time ever that the brilliance of Christmas tree lights was added to ornaments. The warm glow they created was truly special.

The care and attention to detail put into the design of Lighted Ornaments was unsurpassed. As one designer told me, "The only difficulty I had was deciding when the design was complete. I kept on wanting to add more details." Indeed, the designers have added wonderful touches to the ornaments such as real lace trim on the windows of "Santa's Arrival" and the tiny carolers inside the "Village Church."

The beauty of light graced a variety of ornament designs in 1984. Light showed through the windows of a handcrafted house in "Santa's Workshop," lit up the sky of a panorama ball in "Nativity," and even illuminated a traffic signal in "City Lights."

Village Church
This precious clapboard village church looks as if it could have been taken straight from a New England green. The towering spire, topped with a gold cross, rests on a green shingled roof. Candle-lit windows and opened door reveal the inside appointments and holiday carolers.
Handcrafted, 4⅝" tall
1500QLX702-1, $15.00 ☐

Sugarplum Cottage
Sugar-coated gumdrops, lollipops, and peppermint candy canes make this brightly lit cottage look good enough to eat!
Handcrafted, 3" tall
1100QLX701-1, $11.00 ☐

City Lights
To control the flow of forest traffic, Santa and a friendly "traffic squirrel" perch atop the four-way signal that illuminates an animal in each light's surface.
Handcrafted, 3½" tall
1000QLX701-4, $10.00 ☐

Santa's Workshop
Light shines out the window of Santa's workshop as he offers a toy bunny to his cottontail visitor standing outside.
Peek-Through Ball, 3½" diam.
1300QLX700-4, $13.00 ☐

Village Church

Sugarplum Cottage

City Lights

Santa's Workshop

Santa's Arrival
'Tis the night before Christmas and a little boy is sleeping soundly, dreaming of holiday toys. Inside the softly lit room the child's puppy peers out the window and holds up a list of gifts for Santa to read. The window is framed by genuine white eyelet lace.

Peek-Through Ball, 3½" diam.
1300QLX702-4, $13.00 ☐

Nativity
A beautiful vision of that Holy Night. The dark blue of the ball creates a perfect contrast to the warm glow from inside that illuminates the windows of Bethlehem and the Christmas sky. Caption: "Christmas...light through the darkness...love through the ages."

Panorama Ball, 3½" diam.
1200QLX700-1, $12.00 ☐

Stained Glass
Colorful old-fashioned stained glass design glows like a beautiful window when lit.

Golden Classic Shape, 3⅞" diam.
800QLX703-1, $8.00 ☐

Christmas in the Forest
Silver ball evokes the feeling of a moonlit night in a snowy forest. The design looks almost three-dimensional with its varying hues of white, gray and blue, subtly lit from within. Caption: "Christmas ... magical, memorable time of year."

Silver Classic Shape, 3⅞" diam.
800QLX703-4, $8.00 ☐

Brass Carousel
All lit up and reminiscent of an amusement park merry-go-round. You can almost hear the music play as Santa rides by in a gift-laden sleigh pulled by reindeer.

Etched Brass, 3" tall
900QLX707-1, $9.00 ☐

All Are Precious
A delicately etched shepherd, lamb and donkey stand in awe of the brilliant star that sends rays of light over the world. Gold foil-stamped caption: "All are precious in His sight..."

Acrylic, 4" tall
800QLX704-4, $8.00 ☐

Santa's Arrival

Nativity

Stained Glass

Christmas in the Forest

Brass Carousel

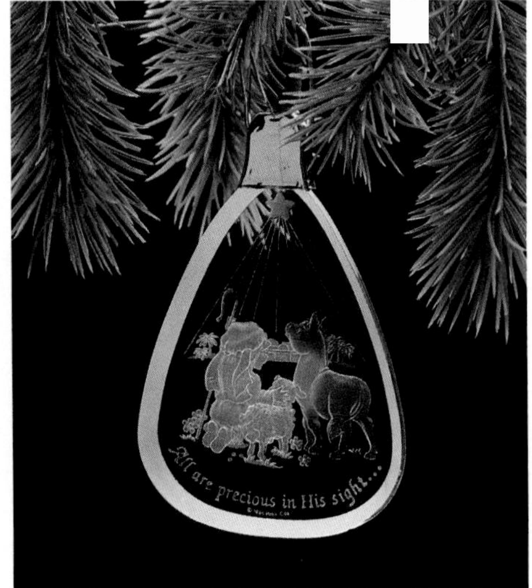

All Are Precious

THE 1985 LIGHTED ORNAMENT COLLECTION

The 1985 Lighted Ornament line was filled with firsts. It contained the first series, the first commemorative, the first property and the first dated ornaments to appear in the new lighted format.

A sleepy mouse reading by candlelight was the first edition in the new "Chris Mouse" Collectible Series. Fashioned to clip onto the tree, this ornament is ideal for people who collect designs of mice as well as series ornaments. The first commemorative in the lighted line was "Baby's First Christmas." This caption, the most popular in the Keepsake line, appeared on a handcrafted carousel complete with acrylic ponies. Both the carousel and the ornament called "Swiss Cheese Lane" were dated "1985." Completing the list of firsts in the Lighted Ornament line was the property "Katybeth." This handcrafted angel was seen painting a beautiful acrylic rainbow, shown to wonderful advantage by the addition of light.

Baby's First Christmas
The carousel is aglow with light as two teddy bears ride 'round and 'round on their frosted acrylic ponies. The ornament is trimmed in gold and displays tiny mirrors on the canopy. Caption: "Baby's First Christmas 1985."

Handcrafted, Acrylic, 4" tall
1650QLX700-5, $16.50 ☐

Katybeth
Both the rainbow and cloud, made of acrylic, light up for the angel Katybeth. She is busily painting the rainbow red, gold and blue so it will shine for the holidays.

Handcrafted, Acrylic, 3⅝" tall
1075QLX710-2, $10.75 ☐

Chris Mouse—First Edition
This little mouse is the first collectible series in the Lighted Ornament line. Dressed in his blue nightshirt, he's reading a Christmas story before bedtime. The candle illuminates his book, dated "1985." The ornament attaches to your tree with a specially designed clip.

Handcrafted, 3⅞" tall
1250QLX703-2, $12.50 ☐

Swiss Cheese Lane
A yellow wedge of Swiss cheese forms the adorable A-frame home for a pair of mice. Through holes in the cheese, you can see the brightly lit interior. One mouse sleeps soundly in a four-poster bed while the other trims the tree in a cozy living room warmed by a potbellied stove and decorated with a braided rug. Caption: "1985 Swiss Cheese Lane."

Handcrafted, 2⅝" tall
1300QLX706-5, $13.00 ☐

Baby's First Christmas

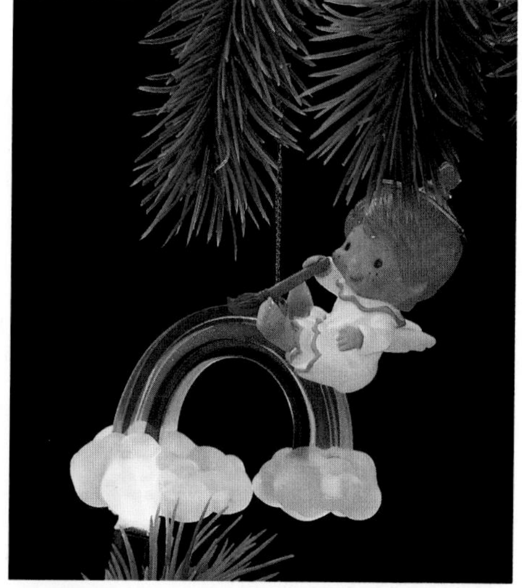

Katybeth

Chris Mouse

Swiss Cheese Lane

Mr. and Mrs. Santa
It's getting late, but Mrs. Santa's home is brightly lit as she trims the tree. Santa waves at passersby from the big picture window and invites us to view the festivities. Inside there's a cozy fireplace with a clock on the mantle and pictures on the wall. The roof is covered with sparkling snow and the chimney wears a holiday wreath. A sign above the door says "The Kringles."

Handcrafted, 3″ tall
1450QLX705-2, $14.50 ☐

Little Red Schoolhouse
The lights are on and the play is about to begin in this intricately detailed schoolhouse. Inside, three parents watch the children perform in a Christmas pageant. Wonderful touches of authenticity include a flagpole in the front, a woodpile at the back, a blackboard inside showing a "chalk" rendition of Bethlehem and a real bell hanging above the front door. A banner announces a "School Play Tonight."

Handcrafted, 2⅝″ tall
1575QLX711-2, $15.75 ☐

Love Wreath
A delicate wreath, decorated with hearts and ribbon, is etched in acrylic and softly illuminated. The special message is stamped in gold foil: "Christmas happens in the heart."

Acrylic, 3½″ tall
850QLX702-5, $8.50 ☐

Sugarplum Cottage
Reissue from 1984. (See 1984 Lighted Ornament Collection.)

Handcrafted, 3″ tall
1100QLX701-1, $11.00

Village Church
Reissue from 1984. (See 1984 Lighted Ornament Collection.)

Handcrafted, 4⅝″ tall
1500QLX702-1, $15.00

Santa's Workshop
Reissue from 1984. (See 1984 Lighted Ornament Collection.)

Peek-Through Ball, 3½″ diam.
1300QLX700-4, $13.00

Nativity
Reissue from 1984. (See 1984 Lighted Ornament Collection.)

Panorama Ball, 3½″ diam.
1200QLX700-1, $12.00

All Are Precious
Reissue from 1984. (See 1984 Lighted Ornament Collection.)

Acrylic, 4″ tall
800QLX704-4, $8.00

Mr. and Mrs. Santa

Little Red Schoolhouse

Love Wreath

Christmas Eve Visit

Christmas Eve Visit
An exquisite, intricately etched brass house glows with light to welcome Santa and his reindeer as they make their rounds on Christmas Eve.

Etched Brass, 2″ tall
1200QLX710-5, $12.00 ☐

Season of Beauty
Blanketed in white, the world reflects the peace and beauty of Christmas. This softly illuminated ornament offers the message, "May joy come into your world as Christmas comes into your heart."

Red and Gold Classic Shape, 3¼″ diam.
800QLX712-2, $8.00 ☐

Season of Beauty

THE 1986 LIGHTED ORNAMENT COLLECTION

Lights! Motion! Action! Hallmark used these three words to describe 1986 Lighted Ornaments and, indeed, the line offered these features and much, much more!

The 1986 ornaments displayed technical advances that quickly enthralled ornament collectors. In addition to light, the designs included electronic motion, scenes that changed before your eyes, and a unique holographic effect.

Two of the ornaments featured motion that was circular. The train in "Village Express" and the sleigh in "Christmas Sleigh Ride" circle scenes under the domes. The motion in "Lighting the Tree" is forward and backward. In this design, Santa moves forward to light the tree and then moves back to his original position.

The "changing scene" feature debuted in the "Baby's First Christmas" ornament. Through the use of alternating lights, it appears as if there are two different scenes inside the panorama ball. Scene one shows a kitten gazing into the empty night sky; scene two shows Santa and his reindeer flying past the window. The new "hologram" feature premiered in the design called "Santa's On His Way." Inside a panorama ball Santa seems to be flying over the city.

Two new Collectible Series were added in '86. The "Sugarplum Fairy" dances in the "Nutcracker Ballet" in the first ornament of the "Christmas Classics" series. And the new "Santa and Sparky" series began with the "light and motion" ornament, "Lighting the Tree."

The commemorative portion of the lighted line increased by three in 1986. The "First Christmas Together" and "Christmas Sleigh Ride" offer romantic designs, and "Sharing Friendship" carries a warm message for a special friend.

Baby's First Christmas

Baby's First Christmas
Sitting in front of the nursery window, by the glowing tree, a kitten looks out into the night. Suddenly Santa and his reindeer appear in the sky to deliver something special for Baby. A light illuminates the first scene and then alternates to the second, creating the magical "changing scene" effect. Caption on Front: "Baby's First Christmas 1986." On Back: "There's someone new on Santa's list, someone small and dear, someone Santa's sure to love and visit every year!"

Panorama Ball, 3⅝" tall
Light and Changing Scene
1950QLX710-3, $19.50 ☐

First Christmas Together

First Christmas Together
A happy teddy bear couple celebrates their first year with a ride in a brightly lit hot-air balloon captioned, "First Christmas Together." Anchoring the basket is a brass heart etched with the date "1986." This caption appears for the first time in the lighted ornament line.

Handcrafted, 5¼" tall
1400QLX707-3, $14.00 ☐

Santa and Sparky

Santa and Sparky — First Edition
Sparky watches eagerly as Santa moves forward and lights the Christmas tree. The excitement of "Lighting the Tree" is just one of the many things Santa will share with his penguin pal each year in this new series. A gift is tagged "1986."

Handcrafted, 4¹⁄₁₆" tall
Light and Motion
2200QLX703-3, $22.00 ☐

Christmas Classics — First Edition
The stage is aglow for the Sugarplum Fairy. She strikes a classic pose and waits for the "Nutcracker Ballet" to begin. Painted in pearly pastels, the stage carries the caption, "Sugarplum Fairy 1986." This series will feature scenes from classic Christmas poems, ballets, or stories.

Handcrafted, 4½" tall
1750QLX704-3, $17.50 ☐

Chris Mouse — Second Edition
A night-light gives this mouse's pinecone bower a cheery glow. His cozy retreat, molded from a real pinecone, is the perfect place for "Chris Mouse Dreams." The treetop address is "1986."

Handcrafted, 3¾" tall
1300QLX705-6, $13.00 ☐

Village Express
A train circles the peaceful mountain village, chugging over the trestle and through the tunnel, as comforting light from the buildings shines across the newly fallen snow.

Handcrafted, 3½" tall
Light and Motion
2450QLX707-2, $24.50 ☐

Christmas Sleigh Ride
The lamp sheds a romantic light on the couple gliding around the park in an old-fashioned sleigh. The bottle-brush trees and dome are sprinkled with snowflakes. Caption: "Love's precious moments shine forever in the heart."

Handcrafted, 3¾" tall
Light and Motion
2450QLX701-2, $24.50 ☐

Santa's On His Way
When you look inside this ornament, it appears as if Santa and his reindeer are magically flying above the city. A silvery hologram, fashioned through laser photography, creates the three-dimensional effect. Caption: "A time of magical moments and dreams come true...Christmas."

Panorama Ball, 3⅝" tall
Light and Hologram
1500QLX711-5, $15.00 ☐

General Store
Warmed by a potbelly stove, this old-fashioned "General Store" is bright and cozy. The woman by the counter may have come in to buy a tree after seeing the sign "Christmas Trees 50¢."

Handcrafted, 2$^{11}/_{16}$" tall
1575QLX705-3, $15.75 ☐

Christmas Classics

Chris Mouse

Village Express

Christmas Sleigh Ride

Santa's On His Way

General Store

Gentle Blessings
The animals in the stable silently gather around the cradle to watch the Baby as He sleeps. Light shines from above, shedding a warm glow on the intricately sculpted scene. Caption: "Baby Jesus, sweetly sleeping, you have blessed our world today."

Panorama Ball, 3 5/8″ tall
1500QLX708-3, $15.00 ☐

Keep on Glowin'!
One of Santa's elves takes time out for some fun and slides down a glowing icicle.

Handcrafted, 2 7/16″ tall
1000QLX707-6, $10.00 ☐

Santa's Snack
Santa has raided the refrigerator! Wearing a striped nightshirt and reindeer slippers, he carries his sandwich creation back to bed. A candle in his hand lights his way.

Handcrafted, 2 15/16″ tall
1000QLX706-6, $10.00 ☐

Merry Christmas Bell
Bathed in soft light, this acrylic bell is decorated with etched holiday flowers and greenery. "Merry Christmas," the universal message of the season, is etched into the center.

Acrylic, 5 9/16″ tall
850QLX709-3, $8.50 ☐

Sharing Friendship
An etched poinsettia provides a festive accent to the gold foil sentiment stamped on this illuminated acrylic teardrop. Caption: "Friendship is a special kind of sharing. 1986."

Acrylic, 5 5/16″ tall
850QLX706-3, $8.50 ☐

Mr. and Mrs. Santa
Reissue from 1985. (See 1985 Lighted Ornament Collection.)

Handcrafted, 3″ tall
1450QLX705-2, $14.50

Sugarplum Cottage
Reissue from 1984. (See 1984 Lighted Ornament Collection.)

Handcrafted, 3″ tall
1100QLX701-1, $11.00

Gentle Blessings

Keep on Glowin'!

Santa's Snack

Merry Christmas Bell

Sharing Friendship

THE 1987 KEEPSAKE MAGIC COLLECTION

In 1987, the Holiday Magic Lighted Ornament Collection was given a new name — the "Keepsake Magic Ornament Collection." In the eyes of collectors, this name change reflected the line's exciting — almost magical — innovations. But what entitled the lighted line to claim the name Keepsake, according to Hallmark, was the increased number of original designs and commemoratives, and the wide variety of features and formats. Hallmark knows that "Keepsake" has come to mean something very special to collectors.

Each "light and motion" ornament in the '87 line displays a different kind of electronic movement. In "Christmas Morning," two children slide down a bannister. Sparky, the penguin in the series ornament "Perfect Portrait," moves forward to illuminate a sculpture of Santa and then retreats to admire his work. And both the man and woman in "Loving Holiday" come out of their house to meet face to face before moving back again.

The "changing scene" ornament this year was "Angelic Messengers." Shepherds watch their flocks under a starry sky until the scene changes, filling the sky with angels. A brand-new feature was "blinking lights," which appeared in the silvery "Good Cheer Blimp."

The 1987 Keepsake Magic line also introduced Hallmark's first lighted photoholder, "Memories Are Forever." The design is festive and suitable for a photo of either an adult or child.

Baby's First Christmas
Trimmed with a lacy fabric curtain, this brightly lit window is the perfect place for Teddy to paint his announcement: "Baby's First Christmas." Baby's blocks on the sill show the date "1987."

Handcrafted, 3¾" tall
1350QLX704-9, $13.50 ☐

First Christmas Together
The igloo glows with light and love. Holding hands by a bottle-brush tree, the polar bear couple celebrates a special Christmas. A red heart displays the year "1987," and "First Christmas Together" is etched in the snow at the top.

Handcrafted, 2⅝" tall
1150QLX708-7, $11.50 ☐

Santa and Sparky—Second Edition
Santa is so pleased with Sparky's latest work of art. Sparky moves forward and lights the sculpture so Santa can see it's a "Perfect Portrait." The pedestal dates the creation "1987."

Handcrafted, 4$^{1}/_{16}$" tall
Light and Motion
1950QLX701-9, $19.50 ☐

Christmas Classics — Second Edition
The elegantly draped stage is set for Dickens' classic work identified in gold on the front: "A Christmas Carol." Illuminated in the center, a happy Scrooge gives gifts to Tiny Tim while Mr. and Mrs. Cratchet look on. Date on Back: "1987"

Handcrafted, 4$^{3}/_{16}$" tall
1600QLX702-9, $16.00 ☐

Baby's First Christmas

First Christmas Together

Santa and Sparky

Christmas Classics

Chris Mouse — Third Edition

Designed to look like stained glass, this lamp sheds a lovely "Chris Mouse Glow." The little mouse has a leather tail and wears a cozy nightshirt dated "87."

Handcrafted, 4⅛" tall
1100QLX705-7, $11.00 ☐

Christmas Morning

It's early morning in this cheery Victorian home, and the tree is lit in anticipation of the children's arrival. They slide down the garland-trimmed bannister eager to open their gifts from Santa.

Handcrafted, 4$^{5}/_{16}$" tall
Light and Motion
2450QLX701-3, $24.50 ☐

Loving Holiday

Light glows softly within this ornament sculpted to resemble an old-fashioned glockenspiel. The loving couple move forward to meet under the clock and then move back, knowing their encounter will be repeated. Caption: "Precious times are spent with those we love."

Handcrafted, 3⅝" tall
Light and Motion
2200QLX701-6, $22.00 ☐

Angelic Messengers

A light shines on the shepherds watching their flocks at night. Then suddenly, the sky is aglow and angels appear, bringing the joyous tidings of Christmas. Light alternates from the shepherds to the angels, creating the "changing scene" effect. Caption: "Love came down at Christmas, love all lovely, love divine. Love was born at Christmas, star and angels gave the sign."

Panorama Ball, 3⅝" tall
Light and Changing Scene
1875QLX711-3, $18.75 ☐

Good Cheer Blimp

The blinking lights on the "Good Cheer Blimp" light the way for Santa on Christmas Eve. He leans over the side of the gondola to spot his next stop. The "blinking-lights" feature appears for the first time in the Keepsake Magic line.

Handcrafted, 3$^{1}/_{16}$" tall
Blinking Lights
1600QLX704-6, $16.00 ☐

Train Station

At the "Train Station" the lights are on, and the ticket window is open for business. A mother and child sit inside where it's warm and cozy while the ticket taker waits for customers. Caption Over Front Door and Side Window: "Merriville." Under Front Window: "Tickets."

Handcrafted, 3$^{3}/_{16}$" tall
1275QLX703-9, $12.75 ☐

Chris Mouse

Christmas Morning

Loving Holiday

Angelic Messengers

Good Cheer Blimp

Train Station

Keeping Cozy
Dressed in flocked long johns, Santa is warmed by the burning embers inside this potbelly stove. A little mouse is keeping warm, too.

Handcrafted, $2\frac{1}{2}$" tall
1175QLX704-7, $11.75 ☐

Lacy Brass Snowflake
Fashioned with two interlocking brass snowflakes, this ornament sparkles with light. The back piece is solid with a delicately etched design. The front piece looks like filigree with its lacy etched and cut-out design.

Brass, $2\frac{1}{2}$" tall
1150QLX709-7, $11.50 ☐

Meowy Christmas!
Two playful kittens frolic on a glowing translucent red heart. They're having a happy holiday time playing with the handcrafted white bow that decorates the ornament.

Handcrafted, $2\frac{1}{2}$" tall
1000QLX708-9, $10.00 ☐

Memories Are Forever Photoholder
This is the first photoholder in the Keepsake Magic line. It illuminates one of your cherished photographs in a frame decorated with red and green bas-relief holly. Caption on Back: "Memory keeps each Christmas forever warm and bright."

Handcrafted, $3\frac{7}{8}$" tall
850QLX706-7, $8.50 ☐

Season for Friendship
The bevel of this acrylic teardrop has a delicately cut design that reflects light like crystal. Christmas greenery etched at the top of the ornament is accented with gold foil berries that complement the matching foil caption: "How lovely the season when it's filled with friendship."

Acrylic, $5\frac{5}{16}$" tall
850QLX706-9, $8.50 ☐

Bright Noel
Within a glowing star, the word "Noel" shines for the holiday. This contemporary acrylic ornament captures the look of neon lighting.

Acrylic, $5\frac{1}{2}$" tall
700QLX705,-9, $7.00 ☐

Village Express
Reissue from 1986. (See 1986 Lighted Ornament Collection.)

Handcrafted, $3\frac{1}{2}$" tall
Light and Motion
2450QLX707-2, $24.50

Keep on Glowin'!
Reissue from 1986. (See 1986 Lighted Ornament Collection.)

Handcrafted, $2\frac{7}{16}$" tall
1000QLX707-6, $10.00

Keeping Cozy

Lacy Brass Snowflake

Meowy Christmas!

Memories Are Forever Photoholder

Season for Friendship

Bright Noel

KEEPSAKE ORNAMENTS: THE ADDED ATTRACTIONS

Collectors notice everything. Through the years, they have discovered several Keepsake Ornaments that were not part of the regular line. These designs were not included in the Keepsake Ornament brochures or displayed with the other Keepsake Ornaments. To say the least, collectors have been intrigued.

To clear up the mystery surrounding these precious odds and ends, I have added the following section to this *Collector's Guide*. It includes the Keepsake Ornaments that have been featured in Hallmark gift and promotional programs such as the "Musical Collection" or "Open House" events. All the designs are "official" Keepsake Ornaments and, grouped together, make quite an interesting mini collection.

Musical Ornaments

The 1982 designs were offered in the Hallmark "Gift Collection," and the 1983 designs in the Hallmark "Musical Collection." All but the "Twelve Days of Christmas" ornament came packaged with an acrylic display stand.

1982

Baby's First Christmas
Baby has a merry time with all the new Christmas toys. The blocks spell out the first word in the caption: "Baby's First Christmas 1982." Melody: "Brahms Lullaby."

Musical, Classic Shape, 4½" tall
1600QMB900-7, $16.00 ☐

First Christmas Together
A sleigh ride in the snow is the perfect way to spend that memorable first Christmas. Caption: "First Christmas Together 1982." Melody: "White Christmas."

Musical, Classic Shape, 4½" tall
1600QMB901-9, $16.00 ☐

Love
Pinecones and holiday greenery decorate a festive ornament that offers a loving melody and message of the season. Caption: "Love puts the warmth in Christmas 1982." Melody: "What the World Needs Now Is Love."

Musical, Classic Shape, 4½" tall
1600QMB900-9, $16.00 ☐

Baby's First Christmas, First Christmas Together, Love

1983

Twelve Days of Christmas
This French blue and white bas-relief design was included in the 1984 Keepsake Ornament collection. Melody: "Twelve Days of Christmas."

Musical, Handcrafted, 3¾" tall
1500QMB415-9, $15.00 ☐

Baby's First Christmas
Dressed in Santa sleepers, the babies on this ornament crawl up and down and all around the candy canes that spell out the caption, "Baby's 1st Christmas 1983." Melody: "Schubert's Lullaby."

Musical, Classic Shape, 4½" tall
1600QMB903-9, $16.00 ☐

Friendship
Muffin celebrates Christmas with her little friends. Caption: "It's song-in-the-air time, lights everywhere time, good fun to share time, it's Christmas." Melody: "We Wish You a Merry Christmas."

Musical, Classic Shape, 4½" tall
1600QMB904-7, $16.00 ☐

Nativity
The Three Kings bring gifts for the Holy Child in this brightly painted Nativity scene. Caption: "The star shone bright with a holy light as heaven came to earth that night." Melody: "Silent Night."

Musical, Classic Shape, 4½" tall
1600QMB904-9, $16.00 ☐

Twelve Days of Christmas, Baby's First Christmas

Friendship, Nativity

Open House Ornaments

Special Keepsake Ornaments were created for the "Open House" events Hallmark dealers held as a festive start to the holiday season.

1986

Santa and His Reindeer
Santa's sleigh is packed, and his reindeer are ready to fly between two branches of your tree, suspended by hooks at both ends of the red cord harness. The ornament can also be displayed on a table or mantel.

Handcrafted, 2" tall and 14" wide
975QXO440-6, $9.75 ☐

Coca-Cola® Santa
Reproduced on porcelain white glass, three nostalgic Coca-Cola paintings show that Santa always has time for his favorite soft drink! Caption: "Memories are reflections of the yesterdays we'll always love. Merry Christmas."

Porcelain White Glass, 2 7/8" diam.
475QXO279-6, $4.75 ☐

Old-Fashioned Santa
Crafted to look like hand-carved wood, this Old-World Santa carries a bag filled with intricately sculpted toys. A little kitten rides in his pocket.

Handcrafted, 4 1/2" tall
1275QXO440-3, $12.75 ☐

Santa's Panda Pal
This lovable flocked panda dresses just like Santa. His red and white knitted hat is topped with a pompom.

Handcrafted, 2 1/4" tall
500QXO441-3, $5.00 ☐

1987

North Pole Power & Light
This hard-working elf uses his shiny metal wrench to light your tree for Christmas. Always ready for an emergency, he carries three colorful replacement bulbs in his pack in case a light goes out.

Handcrafted, 3" tall
627XPR933-3, $10.00 value, $2.95 retail price ☐

Santa and His Reindeer

North Pole Power & Light

Coca-Cola® Santa, Old-Fashioned Santa, Santa's Panda Pal

SANTA CLAUS — THE MOVIE™ Ornaments

Two Keepsake Ornaments were part of a varied group of Hallmark gifts centering on the film. The "Elfmade" emblem appeared on the back of each design stamped in gold foil.

1985

Santa's Village
The movie's magical portrayal of Santa's Village is reproduced in this wintry photograph set in a brass bezel. The caption reads, "Merry, Merry Christmas."

Lacquer-Look, 2¾" tall
675QX300-2, $6.75 ☐

Santa Claus
The sleigh is filled to overflowing with brightly wrapped packages for good girls and boys. Holding the reins, Santa is about to begin his magical journey. Framed in brass, the photograph was taken directly from the movie.

Lacquer-Look, 3½" tall
675QX300-5, $6.75 ☐

Santa's Village, Santa Claus

Gold Crown Ornament

"Gold Crown" is the name of a special Hallmark promotional program. Participating stores offered groups of exclusive gifts and collectibles. The 1986 Gold Crown program included a porcelain Keepsake Ornament.

1986

On The Right Track
Carefully painted by hand, this fine porcelain Santa puts the finishing touches on a toy train. He wears brass spectacles, and his boot carries the artist's signature, "P. Dutkin."

Hand-Painted Fine Porcelain, 4¾" tall
1500QSP420-1, $15.00 ☐

On The Right Track

COLLECTIBLE SERIES

A Collectible Series is a group of ornaments that features a specific design theme or motif, such as the vehicle in the "Here Comes Santa" series. These ornaments are issued one per year for a minimum of three years. Between 1973 and 1987, Hallmark issued twenty-seven official Collectible Series. Twenty-four appeared in the Keepsake Ornament line, and three in the Keepsake Magic line.

Series ornaments are very popular with collectors, and much time and effort go into collecting every edition. The longest-running series was the Betsey Clark ball ornament group that ended with the thirteenth edition in 1985. Seven new series were added in 1986 and 1987. The "Holiday Heirloom" series, included in the 1987 Keepsake Ornament line, was the first to be issued in a limited edition.

Beginning with the Collectible Series ornaments offered in 1982, all series editions are identified with the words, "____in a series" or a tree-shaped symbol with the edition number inside. The symbol is especially helpful in identifying undated series designs and pinpointing their year of issue.

Keepsake Ornament Series

Betsey Clark

The Betsey Clark series is the oldest and longest-running series in the Keepsake Ornament Collection. Starting in 1973 (the year Hallmark introduced its ornaments nationally) and ending with the final Betsey Clark ball ornament in 1985, a total of thirteen ornaments appeared in the series. Other Betsey Clark formats offered have included satin balls, cameo ornaments, handcrafted designs and hand-painted porcelain angels. The series designs shown here are:

1973 250XHD110-2 Christmas 1973
1974 250QX108-1 Musicians
1975 300QX133-1 Caroling Trio
1976 300QX195-1 Christmas 1976
1977 350QX264-2 Truest Joys of Christmas
1978 350QX201-6 Christmas Spirit
1979 350QX201-9 Holiday Fun
1980 400QX215-4 Joy-in-the-Air
1981 450QX802-2 Christmas 1981
1982 450QX215-6 Joys of Christmas
1983 450QX211-9 Christmas Happiness
1984 500QX249-4 Days Are Merry
1985 500QX263-2 Special Kind of Feeling

Betsey Clark: 1973, 1974, 1975

Betsey Clark: 1976, 1977, 1978, 1979

Betsey Clark: 1980, 1981, 1982

Betsey Clark: 1983, 1984, 1985

Betsey Clark: Home for Christmas

The second Betsey Clark ball series features the artist's lovable children celebrating Christmas around the home. The glass balls are 2 ⅞″ in diameter, smaller than those in the first Betsey Clark series.

1986 500QX277-6 Home for Christmas
1987 500QX272-7 Home for Christmas

Betsey Clark: Home For Christmas: 1986, 1987

Tin Locomotive

The Tin Locomotive series, introduced in 1982, is of interest to train, tin and ornament collectors alike. So far the series has depicted six types of locomotives inspired by trains from the early days of American rail transportation.

1982 1300QX460-3 Tin Locomotive
1983 1300QX404-9 Tin Locomotive
1984 1400QX440-4 Tin Locomotive
1985 1475QX497-2 Tin Locomotive
1986 1475QX403-6 Tin Locomotive
1987 1475QX484-9 Tin Locomotive

Tin Locomotive: 1982, 1983

Tin Locomotive: 1984, 1985

Tin Locomotive: 1986, 1987

Thimble

Especially popular with thimble collectors, this whimsical series shows how versatile a thimble can be!

1978	*250QX133-6*	Mouse in a Thimble
1979	*300QX131-9*	A Christmas Salute
1980	*400QX132-1*	Thimble Elf
1981	*450QX413-5*	Thimble Angel
1982	*500QX451-3*	Thimble Mouse
1983	*500QX401-7*	Thimble Elf
1984	*500QX430-4*	Thimble Angel
1985	*550QX472-5*	Thimble Santa
1986	*575QX406-6*	Thimble Partridge
1987	*575QX441-9*	Thimble Drummer

Thimble: 1978, 1979, 1980, 1981, 1982, 1983

Thimble: 1984, 1985, 1986, 1987

Rocking Horse: 1981, 1982, 1983

Rocking Horse: 1984, 1985, 1986, 1987

Rocking Horse

This ever-popular toy, cherished by generations of children, has found favor in a new form. Each year the Rocking Horse series features a different steed with flying mane and tail of yarn.

1981 900QX422-2 Dappled
1982 1000QX502-3 Black
1983 1000QX417-7 Russett
1984 1000QX435-4 Appaloosa
1985 1075QX493-2 Pinto
1986 1075QX401-6 Palomino
1987 1075QX482-9 White

Carrousel

The Carrousel series depicts fun and frolic on a colorful, rotating carrousel. This is one of the series most sought after by collectors. The 1983 design was the final edition.

1978 600QX146-3 Antique Toys
1979 650QX146-7 Christmas Carrousel
1980 750QX141-4 Merry Carrousel
1981 900QX427-5 Skaters' Carrousel
1982 1000QX478-3 Snowman Carrousel
1983 1100QX401-9 Santa and Friends

Carrousel: 1978, 1979, 1980

Carrousel: 1981, 1982, 1983

Norman Rockwell: 1980, 1981, 1982

Norman Rockwell: 1983, 1984, 1985

Norman Rockwell: 1986, 1987

Norman Rockwell

The art of Norman Rockwell is known and loved by all, and this delightful series of cameos presents the artist's vision of Christmas in a beautiful dimension. In addition to the cameo series, Rockwell artwork has been featured on glass and satin ball ornaments since 1974. The cameo series designs shown here are:

1980 650QX306-1 Santa's Visitors
1981 850QX511-5 The Carolers
1982 850QX305-3 Filling the Stockings
1983 750QX300-7 Dress Rehearsal
1984 750QX341-1 Caught Napping
1985 750QX374-5 Postman and Kids
1986 775QX321-3 Checking Up
1987 775QX370-7 The Christmas Dance

Here Comes Santa

The Here Comes Santa collection proves that Santa is capable of using any mode of transportation to make his Christmas Eve deliveries.

1979	*900QX155-9*	*Santa's Motorcar*
1980	*1200QX143-4*	*Santa's Express*
1981	*1300QX438-2*	*Rooftop Deliveries*
1982	*1500QX464-3*	*Jolly Trolley*
1983	*1300QX403-7*	*Santa Express*
1984	*1300QX432-4*	*Santa's Deliveries*
1985	*1400QX496-5*	*Santa's Fire Engine*
1986	*1400QX404-3*	*Kringle's Kool Treats*
1987	*1400QX484-7*	*Santa's Woody*

Here Comes Santa: 1979, 1980, 1981

Here Comes Santa: 1982, 1983, 1984, 1985

Here Comes Santa: 1986, 1987

Holiday Wildlife

The Holiday Wildlife series, introduced in 1982, is especially appealing to bird watchers who appreciate skillful and true-to-life artistic representations of beautiful birds. The paintings are reproduced on a white, porcelain-like insert and are framed and backed in natural wood.

1982	*700QX313-3*	*Cardinalis, Cardinalis*
1983	*700QX309-9*	*Black-Capped Chickadees*
1984	*725QX347-4*	*Ring-Necked Pheasant*
1985	*750QX376-5*	*California Quail*
1986	*750QX321-6*	*Cedar Waxwing*
1987	*750QX371-7*	*Snow Goose*

Holiday Wildlife: 1982, 1983, 1984

Holiday Wildlife: 1985, 1986, 1987

Miniature Creche

A series of unique Nativities fashioned in different media such as wood and porcelain.

1985	*875QX482-5*	*Wood and Woven Straw*
1986	*900QX407-6*	*Fine Porcelain*
1987	*900QX481-9*	*Multi-Plated Brass*

Miniature Creche: 1985, 1986, 1987

SNOOPY® and Friends

SNOOPY®, in a three-dimensional format, made his debut in 1979 in an exciting peek-through ball ornament. The "window" in this ball ornament allows you to peek in on SNOOPY's® holiday antics. The 1983 edition is the final ornament in this series.

1979 800QX141-9 Ice-Hockey Holiday
1980 900QX154-1 Ski Holiday
1981 1200QX436-2 SNOOPY® and Friends
1982 1300QX480-3 SNOOPY® and Friends
1983 1300QX416-9 Santa SNOOPY®

SNOOPY® and Friends: 1979, 1980

SNOOPY® and Friends: 1983

SNOOPY® and Friends: 1981, 1982

Windows of the World

A series which depicts international celebrations of Christmas by children, including holiday greetings in a different language each year.

1985 975QX490-2 Feliz Navidad
1986 1000QX408-3 Vrolyk Kerstfeest
1987 1000QX482-7 Mele Kalikimaka

Windows of the World: 1985, 1986, 1987

Nostalgic Houses and Shops

The Nostalgic Houses and Shops series was introduced in 1984. Each piece is carefully researched so that the detailing is both authentic and accurate.

1984	*1300QX448-1*	*Victorian Dollhouse*
1985	*1375QX497-5*	*Old-Fashioned Toy Shop*
1986	*1375QX403-3*	*Christmas Candy Shoppe*
1987	*1400QX483-9*	*House on Main St.*

Nostalgic Houses and Shops: 1984, 1985

Nostalgic Houses and Shops: 1986, 1987

Wood Childhood Ornaments

These nostalgic wooden ornaments from yesteryear feature special authentic touches such as wheels that turn and bows made of fabric.

1984	*650QX439-4*	*Wooden Lamb*
1985	*700QX472-2*	*Wooden Train*
1986	*750QX407-3*	*Wooden Reindeer*
1987	*750QX441-7*	*Wooden Horse*

Wood Childhood Ornaments: 1984, 1987, 1985, 1986

Twelve Days of Christmas

This acrylic series depicts Hallmark's interpretation of each of the twelve days in the favorite Christmas carol.

1984	*600QX348-4*	*Partridge in a Pear Tree*
1985	*650QX371-2*	*Two Turtle Doves*
1986	*650QX378-6*	*Three French Hens*
1987	*650QX370-9*	*Four Colly Birds*

Twelve Days of Christmas: 1984, 1985

Twelve Days of Christmas: 1986, 1987

Porcelain Bear

For teddy bear lovers especially, an annual porcelain edition of a lovable bear named Cinnamon. Each bear is carefully painted by hand.

1983	*700QX428-9*	Cinnamon Teddy
1984	*700QX454-1*	Cinnamon Bear
1985	*750QX479-2*	Cinnamon Bear
1986	*775QX405-6*	Cinnamon Bear
1987	*775QX442-7*	Cinnamon Bear

Porcelain Bear: 1983, 1984, 1985, 1986, 1987

The Bellringers

Holiday bells have a touch of whimsy in this unique series that brings a new interpretation to this traditional design motif. Made of fine porcelain, the bells have different handcrafted clappers each year. The sixth and last of The Bellringer series was produced in 1984.

1979 1000QX147-9 The Bellswinger
1980 1500QX157-4 The Bellringers
1981 1500QX441-5 Swingin' Bellringer
1982 1500QX455-6 Angel Bellringer
1983 1500QX403-9 Teddy Bellringer
1984 1500QX438-4 Elfin Artist

Bellringer: 1979, 1980, 1981

Bellringer: 1982, 1983, 1984

Art Masterpiece

This padded satin series offers reproductions of religious fine art masterpieces from around the world. The series ended in 1986.

1984 650QX349-4 Madonna and Child and St. John
1985 675QX377-2 Madonna of the Pomegranate
1986 675QX350-6 Madonna and Child with the Infant St. John

Art Masterpiece: 1984, 1985, 1986

Frosty Friends

Each design in the Frosty Friends series depicts a form of winter-wonderland fun in Santa's frosty North Pole neighborhood.

1980	*650QX137-4*	*A Cool Yule*
1981	*800QX433-5*	*Frosty Friends*
1982	*800QX452-3*	*Frosty Friends*
1983	*800QX400-7*	*Frosty Friends*
1984	*800QX437-1*	*Frosty Friends*
1985	*850QX482-2*	*Frosty Friends*
1986	*850QX405-3*	*Frosty Friends*
1987	*850QX440-9*	*Frosty Friends*

Frosty Friends: 1980, 1981, 1982, 1983

Frosty Friends: 1984, 1985, 1986, 1987

Clothespin Soldier

The Clothespin Soldier series features a soldier wearing a different uniform each year. The final ornament was issued in 1987.

1982	*500QX458-3*	*British*
1983	*500QX402-9*	*Early American*
1984	*500QX447-1*	*Canadian Mountie*
1985	*550QX471-5*	*Scottish Highlander*
1986	*550QX406-3*	*French Officer*
1987	*550QX480-7*	*Sailor*

Clothespin Soldier: 1982, 1983, 1984, 1985, 1986, 1987

Mr. and Mrs. Claus: 1986, 1987

Mr. and Mrs. Claus

Santa and his lovely spouse appear in your home to show how they celebrate Christmas in the Claus houlehold.

1986 1300QX402-6 Merry Mistletoe Time
1987 1325QX483-7 Home Cooking

Reindeer Champs: 1986, 1987

Reindeer Champs

Santa's team of reindeer champions appears in a series that will feature a different sport each year.

1986 750QX422-3 Dasher
1987 750QX480-9 Dancer

Collector's Plate: 1987

Holiday Heirloom: 1987

Collector's Plate

The heartwarming artwork on this series of miniature fine porcelain collector's plates depicts the excitement, joy and anticipation children experience at Christmas.

1987 800QX481-7 Light Shines at Christmas

Holiday Heirloom

This series marks several firsts. It is the first limited edition series and the first to feature lead crystal and a precious metal. Each ornament will combine an intricately sculpted silver-plated design with a 24 percent lead crystal bell in an edition limited to 34,600 pieces.

1987 2500QX485-7 Holiday Heirloom

Keepsake Magic Series

Chris Mouse

This is the first series to feature light. The little mouse sitting by the candle and other mice in future years will both decorate and light your tree.

1985	*1250QLX703-2*	Chris Mouse
1986	*1300QLX705-6*	Chris Mouse Dreams
1987	*1100QLX705-7*	Chris Mouse Glow

Chris Mouse: 1985, 1986, 1987

Santa and Sparky

Santa and his penguin pal Sparky share the fun of Christmas in this first "light and motion" series.

1986	*2200QLX703-3*	*Lighting the Tree*
1987	*2200QLX701-9*	*Perfect Portrait*

Santa and Sparky: 1986, 1987

Christmas Classics

This series of lighted three-dimensional scenes illustrates beloved Christmas stories, ballets, books, poems and songs.

1986	*1750QLX704-3*	*The Nutcracker Ballet — Sugarplum Fairy*
1987	*1600QLX702-9*	*A Christmas Carol*

Christmas Classics: 1986, 1987

INDEX

ABOUT THE AUTHOR

Few modern day art forms have enjoyed more of a renaissance than Christmas ornaments. Over the past decade, the little stars, bells and other holiday mementos that normally spend eleven months of the year in the attic have become prized collectors' items.

At the forefront of this movement has been Hallmark. With its vast team of creative artists and designers, Hallmark has virtually redecorated the American Christmas tree, turning it into a wonderland of delightful holiday keepsakes.

The author, Clara Johnson Scroggins, has collected ornaments since 1973, the same year Hallmark started its Keepsake Collection. Intrigued at first solely with silver tree trimmers, Mrs. Scroggins branched into collecting ornaments made by other manufacturers and has amassed a private collection of more than 30,000 individual ornaments.

A meticulous historian, Mrs. Scroggins is considered by many to be the premiere authority on American Christmas ornaments. The author of a collector's guide to silver ornaments and other articles on collecting, she frequently is on the lecture circuit, speaking to collectors' groups and appearing on radio and television.

Mrs. Scroggins was born in Lake Village, Arkansas, and is a former high-fashion model and broadcast journalist. Her interests include art and antiques. She and her husband, Joe, have one son and a granddaughter and reside in Houston.

Hallmark Keepsake Ornaments: A Collector's Guide

Third edition written by Clara Johnson Scroggins
Editor: Tina Hacker
Cover Design: Rita Guile
Page Design: Sarah Taylor